1961

FROM AN IVORY TOWER

FROM AN IVORY TOWER is one of the volumes in a new series, IMPACT BOOKS, designed to bring to the modern reader the significant achievements of scholars, both Catholic and non-Catholic, in the fields of Scripture, Theology, Philosophy, Mathematics, History, and the Physical and Social Sciences. IMPACT BOOKS will explore these realms of human knowledge in order to give the average man some idea of the work being carried on today within them and in order to lay a basis for fruitful dialogue between men of different interests and persuasions on questions vital to all mankind.

FROM AN IVORY TOWER

A Discussion of Philosophical Problems Originating in Modern Mathematics

Bernard A. Hausmann, S.J.

THE BRUCE PUBLISHING COMPANY
MILWAUKEE

Library of Congress Catalog Card Number: 60–12928

© 1960 THE BRUCE PUBLISHING COMPANY
Made in the United States of America

510.1
H375

Preface

One who knows no more of mathematics than what he may have learned in high school may wonder how any mathematical truth can have a philosophical or theological implication. It requires only a slight acquaintance with the writings of modern philosophers to show how the discoveries of mathematicians have been utilized to defend untenable philosophical theories. For example, Professor Morris R. Cohen advances modern mathematical discoveries to support his attack on the first principles of self-evident truths advanced by Catholic ethicians:[1]

> In a Catholic manual of socialism, we have a long list of such eternal first principles, which are put in the same class with such axioms as "The whole is greater than any part," "The cause must be equal to the effect," and the like. As the model for this view is presented by the Euclidean geometry it is suggestive to apply to these self-evident axioms the criticism which modern mathematics has applied to the Euclidean system. The discovery of non-Euclidean geometry and the whole trend of modern mathematical thought has led us to discard as unreliable the self-evident character of axioms or principles. Such principles as that two magnitudes equal to the same are equal to each other, or that a straight line is the shortest distance between two points, are seen to be simply definitions, while others are either hypotheses or assumptions or else rules of procedure or postulates, whose contraries may not only be just as conceivable but even preferable in certain systems of mechanics. If now we apply the same criticism to our assumed principles of natural law, such as "All men are equal before the law," or "All men have the right to life, to the product of their labour," etc., it becomes evident that the only way to defend them against those who would deny them is to show that like other scientific principles, e.g., the Copernican hypothesis in astronomy, they yield a body or system of propositions which is preferable to that which can possibly be established on the basis of their denial.

---

[1] *Reason and Nature* (New York: Harcourt, Brace & Co., 1931), p. 413.

v

30665

Another attack on the same target comes from the pen of Professor Max Black:[2]

> To say that a principle is "self-evident" is to say that it does not need the evidence of any *other* proposition. The principle, then, is perceived to be true as soon as it is "fully understood." . . . It is all the more striking, therefore, that hardly a belief that has been held self-evident to some people has not been held false by others. At various times, men have believed that it was self-evident that the earth was flat, that some women were witches, that infants dying without baptism were doomed to eternal damnation, and that all animals belonged to divinely created and eternally unchangeable kinds. (If you believe in none of these, it would be useful to consider whether you believe that a whole must be greater than its parts, or that space must be infinite. For both of these, like our proposition concerning the crossing of straight lines, are not accepted as true by modern scientists without reservations.) In short, belief that a proposition is self-evident, however strong that belief may be, is no guarantee that the belief is true.

To answer the arguments of men of this stamp, we must first know something of Euclidean geometry, because it was the study of this geometry which led to the discovery of non-Euclidean geometries. Next we must know something of these non-Euclidean geometries and of the problem which their discovery raised, for it is precisely the discovery of these geometries which changed mathematics from the mathematics of old to modern mathematics. We shall do all this in the first five chapters. After that we shall consider some special topics in mathematics which present their own philosophical problems.

Since this book is intended for nonmathematicians, efforts have been made to avoid the technicalities and elisions which would please mathematicians and only mystify the lay reader.

---

[2] *Critical Thinking* (New York: Prentice-Hall, 1946), pp. 238–239.

Contents

FROM AN IVORY TOWER

CHAPTER I

Euclidean Geometry

We owe the science of geometry to the genius of the Greeks. There was a rudimentary geometry in Egypt where the annual floods of the Nile, which destroyed all man-made boundary marks of individual fields, made it necessary for the Egyptians to replace them each year. This geometry consisted for the most part in certain rules of thumb useful in mensuration. The only proofs for the rules seem to have been pragmatic: the rules worked sufficiently well. The Greeks took over these rules and in a remarkably short time, probably a century and a half, presented the world with a finished science. It would be interesting if we could follow the growth and development of the science of geometry, but that is impossible. We meet it for the first time as a fully developed science in the thirteen books of Euclid's *Elements of Geometry.*

We know very little about Euclid himself. He lived about 300 B.C. Where or when he was born and when he died has not been determined. He was probably educated at Athens. The first Ptolemy invited him to teach at Alexandria. Some charming stories are told of him. When Ptolemy asked him for the royal road to geometry, he is said to have told him that there was no royal road; that king and commoner had to travel the same road to arrive at a knowledge of geometry. When one of his pupils, evidently of a very practical turn of mind, wanted to know what he would gain by his study of geometry, Euclid is said to have instructed one of his slaves to give the student a coin for each theorem well learned.

The *Elements of Geometry* of Euclid is a most remarkable work. It supplanted all other treatises on geometry that preceded his, and has been used as a textbook of geometry down to our own times. Certainly twenty-two centuries is a very long life for a textbook. Many and perhaps most of the theorems of the *Elements* Euclid borrowed from his predecessors, though some are doubtless original. However the choice of postulates and the arrangement of the propositions seem to have been his. Many geometries have been written since Euclid's time. They are all adaptations of Euclid, and most of them compare with the original as a student's copy compares with the master's work.

To understand modern mathematics we must know something of non-Euclidean geometries. But we cannot understand the latter unless we first understand classic Euclidean geometry. This can best be learned from Euclid's own *Elements*. The most authoritative text of Euclid's *Elements* in the original Greek is that by Heiberg. The most authoritative English translation is by T. L. Heath. We shall follow the latter.[1]

To understand the text of Euclid we must read it in its historical context. Modern readers are all too apt to read it in the light of the twentieth century, and to hold Euclid responsible for not having made all the geometrical discoveries of the intervening 22 centuries. Again, the modern mind is often afflicted with the cult of science, which manifests itself in cultivating science for science's sake and not for the truth it contains and the light it throws on the universe in which we live. Such an attitude was foreign to the Greek mind in Euclid's day. The Greeks were curious about the universe in which they found themselves. To learn more about it, they created their sciences. For them they were tools or means to an end, and they used them as such.

The statement is often made that Euclid's *Elements* is the first example of a deductive science which has come down to us. If the adjective mathematical is added, the statement is true enough. But Aristotle's philosophy is as much a deductive science

---

[1] We quote with permission from *The Thirteen Books of Euclid's Elements* by Thomas L. Heath. Dover Publications, New York ($6.00), 3 volumes.

4

as Euclid's geometry. They were both born of the desire to know more about the universe in which we live. Without the former, the latter would have been impossible.

Actually there is a reason why the first sciences developed by man proved to be deductive. When man first began to employ leisure to satisfy his natural curiosity about the universe, there were, of course, no scientific instruments, few experiments that he could perform, no accumulation of observations from which he could deduce principles on which to build an inductive science. Reflection, however, did bring to light certain first principles and fundamental truths. Further reflection elaborated these into deductive sciences. Not that the Greeks did not attempt inductive sciences, but their efforts in this direction did not lead to even a near approximation of the truth. Their deductive sciences, however, are as valid today as they were when they were first put together by these early Greek pioneers.

There is no preface or introduction to Euclid's *Elements*, and there are no comments. What we get is a complete science unadorned. Either an introduction and commentary was not needed by Euclid's readers, or it was to be supplied by the teacher. To supply this want now means that we must strive as far as possible to enter into the life and times of the early Greeks.

The first book of the *Elements* begins with 23 definitions.[2] The first seven of these are:

1. A *point* is that which has no part.
2. A *line* is breadthless length.
3. The extremities of a line are points.
4. A *straight line* is a line which lies evenly with the points on itself.
5. A *surface* is that which has length and breadth only.
6. The extremities of a surface are lines.
7. A *plane surface* is a surface which lies evenly with the straight lines on itself.

To appreciate these definitions, suppose that you lived before the days when there was any geometry. In your travels you had

---

[2] In the appendix we give the complete text except for the proofs of the propositions.

5

learned from the Egyptians that one of the angles in a triangle whose sides are in the ratio of $3:4:5$ is always a right angle. You experimented by constructing various triangles with sides of wood, or rope, or by drawing such triangles in the sand or on a tablet. You found the statement to be true enough. You asked yourself why this must be so. If you had the talent and inspiration of the early Greeks, you would realize sooner or later that to make any progress the elements of your triangles would have to be idealized. The lines of your triangle would have to have length but no width, the ends of the lines must be points with no dimensions but only position, the triangles would have to be conceived as drawn on a plane which has length and breadth but no thickness. Such idealization is necessary if there is to be a geometry. It required real genius to reach this conclusion. Who made it first we do not know. The purpose of Euclid's first seven definitions is to give us this idealization. They give us the elements about which and with which the science of geometry will be constructed.

It is well to distinguish the first seven definitions of Euclid from the remaining sixteen. The first seven are more properly descriptions of the elements with which the science of geometry will be concerned. The remaining Euclidean definitions more properly merit the title of definition, since they explain more complicated geometrical concepts in terms of simpler ones. This is illustrated by the following definitions.

10. When a straight line set up on a straight line makes the adjacent angles equal to one another, each of the equal angles is *right*, and the straight line standing on the other is called a *perpendicular* to that on which it stands.

15. A *circle* is a plane figure contained by one line such that all the straight lines falling upon it from one point among those lying within the figure are equal to one another.

20. Of trilateral figures, an *equilateral triangle* is that which has its three sides equal, and *isosceles triangle* is that which has two of its sides alone equal, and a *scalene triangle* that which has its three sides unequal.

The problem of definition and the role it plays in any science

6

was considered by Aristotle. One of his distinctions pertinent to the science of geometry is that between a real and a nominal definition. This distinction is important, for only real definitions may be used in the proof of any proposition. A nominal definition merely tells us what we mean by a certain term. It lists a number of properties which are henceforth to be known by the new name. Definition 20 above is a good example of a nominal definition. A real definition, however, not only tells us what we mean by a term but also assures us that the properties we summarize by the new term are consistent, and that as a result the thing we have defined can exist. However, the proof of the consistency of the properties is not put into the definition. Hence, we can distinguish a nominal definition from a real definition only if we know that a proof of the consistency of the properties has been given or that the object defined actually exists. The nominal definition of an equilateral triangle above will become real as soon as we show how such a triangle can be constructed. Euclid will do this in his first proposition. Euclid is most careful in this matter. He never uses a definition in a proof until he has made that definition a real definition.

By way of illustration, suppose that we define a 2–3–6 triangle to be a triangle whose sides are respectively 2, 3, and 6 units in length. Let us now try to prove that there are triangles whose sides are respectively 4, 6, and 12 units in length. Let us further suppose that we have already established the existence of similar triangles, i.e., triangles whose sides are respectively proportional. We then note that the sides of the triangle whose existence we wish to prove are exactly twice as long as the 2–3–6 triangle we have defined. Therefore, we conclude that such triangles are possible. The proof, of course, is invalid. It is invalid precisely because we have used a nominal definition in our proof, without previously making it a real definition. If we now try to make this definition real in order to validate our proof, we shall find that this cannot be done. In any triangle the sum of the lengths of any two of its sides must always be greater than the third side. Hence there is no 2–3–6 triangle possible, and our nominal definition cannot be made real.

We list Euclid's definition of parallel lines because of the

7

part it played in the discovery of non-Euclidean geometries.

23. *Parallel* straight lines are straight lines which, being in the same plane and being produced indefinitely in both directions, do not meet one another in either direction.

Other definitions of parallel lines have been suggested and used in the centuries since Euclid. Euclid's definition still seems the best and least open to criticism.

After the definitions in Euclid's *Elements* we find two lists of propositions, one titled *postulates* and the other *common notions*. They are propositions which Euclid will not prove, but will use to prove the propositions of his geometry. They are the foundation stones on which Euclid will erect his mansion of geometry. They are:

The Postulates

1. To draw a straight line from any point to any point.
2. To produce a finite straight line continuously in a straight line.
3. To describe a circle with any center and distance.
4. That all right angles are equal to one another.
5. That, if a straight line falling on two straight lines make the interior angles on the same side less than two right angles, the two straight lines, if produced indefinitely, meet on that side on which are the angles less than the two right angles.

The Common Notions

1. Things which are equal to the same thing are also equal to one another.
2. If equal be added to equal, the wholes are equal.
3. If equal be subtracted from equals, the remainders are equal.
4. Things which coincide with one another are equal to one another.
5. The whole is greater than the part.

A question presents itself at once: Why are there two lists of propositions? Why not combine them into a single list? The answer seems to be that the postulates are all strictly geometrical propositions, whereas the common notions are not strictly geometrical, since they also have applications in other fields.

Even the modern mathematician sometimes distinguishes between postulates and axioms. When a distinction is made between these two terms, then a postulate is a proposition about the elements of the given science, while an axiom is any proposition from another science which is necessary in the given science.

The most important question concerning the postulates and common notions of Euclid is this: How are these propositions to be viewed? Are they mere assumptions which the reader is to grant, or are they propositions which enunciate truths? Are they self-evident truths? To begin with, there can be no doubt that these fundamental propositions are not mere assumptions for Euclid and his contemporaries. The Greeks were primarily interested in truth, in learning the facts about the universe. There is not a single instance where they developed conclusions from premises which were purely arbitrary just to see what conclusions could be drawn. That exercise was left by them for the modern mathematician. But if the postulates enunciate truths, and they must if the science built on them is to be true, they must be self-evident truths, since the postulates are not proved in either geometry or any antecedent science.

What is a self-evident proposition? We may say that a proposition is self-evident if it requires no other proposition or propositions to establish its truth. That means that as soon as we know the subject and the predicate of such a proposition, we can affirm or deny the relation between them. Thus to take Euclid's common notion five, "The whole is greater than a part." Once I know what whole means and what part means, I cannot do otherwise than accept the proposition. The notions of whole and of part, however, are obtained from experience. It is only after I have examined a great many finite wholes and have become familiar with their finite, proper parts, that the truth of the proposition becomes evident to me. This means that for Euclid the elements point, straight line, plane were realities with very definite properties, even though they existed only in the mental order. These properties were not assigned to them by the mind, but rather abstracted by the mind from realities. Thus, among many lines

9

drawn some had more curvature than others. Those with no curvature were called straight. The important thing to remember is that for Euclid the postulates did not assign properties to lines, points, and planes, but rather listed properties of points, lines, and planes gathered from observation and experience. We shall examine some of the postulates from this point of view.

The first postulate tells us that any two points can be joined by a straight line. Before this proposition can be accepted about mathematical points and straight lines, we must have a wide experience in drawing points and lines, which, of course, will not be mathematical points and lines. We must have experience in joining points with lines of various shapes. We must have used a straightedge to join points. In the light of this experience with nonmathematical points and lines, the truth of the postulate about mathematical points and lines becomes evident. We admit the proposition not for the sake of argument, but as actually true. The proposition has not been established as a conclusion from other propositions. Hence, it enunciates a self-evident truth about Euclidean points and straight lines.

Anyone who has tried to lengthen a straight line segment that he has drawn will admit that this cannot be done with perfect accuracy. That it can be done with mathematical lines Euclid states in his second postulate. The truth stated here is that we can conceive of a line as prolonged.

The compass that Euclid used was, no doubt, a very crude instrument judged by modern standards, but that compass was merely a tool to draw curves which approximated an ideal circle. Postulate three states that the mathematician can conceive of a perfect circle as drawn with any center and any prescribed radius. The center and radius are designated by two distinct points, one of which will be the center and the other a point on the circumference of the circle. So the postulate states the truth that from figures crudely drawn to represent circles, the mind can abstract from the imperfections and conceive a perfect circle of any size and in any position.

Euclid's fifth postulate differs from the other four in several ways. It certainly lacks the simplicity and brevity of the others. In addition it is the converse of proposition 17 of book one. It

10

would be difficult to show that this postulate is self-evident. At any rate, a very great number of mathematicians down the centuries have attempted to prove this postulate as a proposition. As a result we know many other propositions which could replace Euclid's fifth postulate. In practice it has been so replaced in most high school texts of Euclidean geometry. It is done by assuming Euclid's 29th proposition, in the proof of which he uses the fifth postulate. The new postulate assumes that only one parallel to a given line can be drawn through a given point not on the line. There can be no doubt, however, that for Euclid the fifth postulate was more than a mere assumption. For him it enunciated a truth.

After the postulates and common notions, Euclid at once begins to prove the propositions of geometry. He divides these propositions into thirteen books. There will be more definitions, but these will always be found before the propositions of the particular book in which they are to be used. It will be adequate for our purpose to examine only a few of the 48 propositions of the first book.

"*Proposition 1. On a given finite straight line to construct an equilateral triangle.*

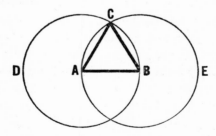

"Let AB be the given finite straight line. Thus it is required to construct an equilateral triangle on the straight line AB.

"With center A and distance AB let the circle BCD be described (P. 3); again, with center B and distance BA let the circle ACE be described (P. 3); and from the point C, in which the circles cut one another, to the points A, B let the straight lines CA, CB be joined (P. 1). Now since the point A is the center of the circle CDB, AC is equal to AB (Def. 15). Again,

11

since the point B is the center of the circle CAE, BC is equal to BA (Def. 15). But CA was also equal to AB; therefore each of the straight lines CA, CB is equal to AB. And things which are equal to the same things are also equal to one another (C.N. 1). Therefore CA is also equal to CB. Therefore the three straight lines CA, AB, BC are equal to one another. Therefore the triangle ABC is equilateral; and it has been constructed on the given finite straight line AB. (Being) what it was required to do."

Euclid follows a fixed pattern in each of his propositions. He begins by listing what is given and what has to be done if the proposition concerns a construction, or what must be proved if the proposition states a fact. Each proposition will conclude with a summary of the proposition and the words "(Being) what it was required to do" in propositions concerning constructions, or with the words "(Being) what it was required to prove" in propositions of affirmation. It has long been customary to translate these phrases into the Latin *Quod erat faciendum* and *Quod erat demonstrandum*, and then to use only the first letters of each word, so that each proposition ends with either $Q.E.F.$ or $Q.E.D.$

Euclid draws the figures to illustrate his propositions. He does not argue from the drawn figures, but from the idealized figures which they represent. He frequently uses these figures and their obvious properties in his proof, as he does in this first proposition. Such procedure could shock the delicate conscience of a modern mathematician who may use only his postulates in the proof of any proposition. It also puts undue strain on the structure of geometry as a purely deductive science. But Euclid had no misgivings about his method. He was interested not in constructing a perfect, deductive science, but rather in discovering the truth about geometric configurations, and any means that contributed to that end was grist for his mill.

"*Proposition 4. If two triangles have the two sides equal to two sides respectively, and have the angles contained by the equal straight lines equal, they will also have the base equal to the base, the triangle will be equal to the triangle, and the*

12

remaining angles will be equal to the remaining angles respectively, namely those which the equal sides subtend.

"Let ABC, DEF be two triangles having the two sides AB, AC equal to the two sides DE, DF respectively, namely AB to DE and AC to DF, and the angle BAC equal to the angle EDF.

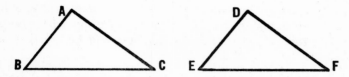

"I say that the base BC is also equal to the base EF, the triangle ABC will be equal to the triangle DEF, and the remaining angles will be equal to the remaining angles respectively, namely those which the equal sides subtend, that is, the angle ABC to the angle DEF, and the angle ACB to the angle DFE.

"For, if the triangle ABC be applied to the triangle DEF, and if the point A be placed on the point D and the straight line AB on DE, then the point B will also coincide with E, because AB is equal to DE.

"Again, AB coinciding with DE, the straight line AC will also coincide with DF, because the angle BAC is equal to the angle EDF; hence the point C will also coincide with the point F, because AC is again equal to DF. But B also coincided with E; hence the base BC will coincide with the base EF. [For if, when B coincides with E and C with F, the base BC does not coincide with the base EF, two straight lines will enclose a space: which is impossible. Therefore the base BC will coincide with EF] and will be equal to it (C.N. 4). Thus the whole triangle ABC will coincide with the whole triangle DEF, and will be equal to it. And the remaining angles will also coincide with the remaining angles and will be equal to them, the angle ABC to the angle DEF, and the angle ACB to the angle DFE. Therefore, etc. (Being) what it was required to prove."

In this proposition we find a survival of a method of proof by superposition, very commonly used when geometry was suffering from growing pains. It is a method that Euclid does not like, and he uses other methods whenever he can.

13

The part of the proof enclosed in brackets is certainly an interpolation. The argument it presents is not necessary for the proof of the theorem if the first postulate is understood in the sense which Euclid undoubtedly assigned to it, namely, that one and only one straight line can be drawn between two points.

"*Proposition 5. In isosceles triangles the angles at the base are equal to one another, and, if the equal straight lines be produced further, the angles under the base will be equal to one another.*

"Let ABC be an isosceles triangle having the side AB equal

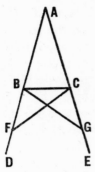

to the side AC; and let the straight lines BD, CE be produced further in a straight line with AB, AC (P. 2). I say that the angle ABC is equal to the angle ACB, and the angle CBD to the angle BCE.

"Let a point F be taken at random on BD; from AE the greater let AG be cut off equal to AF the less (Prop. 3); and let the straight lines FC, GB be joined (P. 1). Then, since AF is equal to AG and AB to AC, the two sides FA, AC are equal to the two sides GA, AB, respectively; and they contain a common angle, the angle FAG. Therefore the base FC is equal to the base GB, and the triangle AFC is equal to the triangle AGB, and the remaining angles will be equal to the remaining angles respectively, namely those which the equal sides subtend, that is, the angle ACF to the angle ABG, and the angle AFC to the angle AGB (Prop. 4). And since the whole AF is equal to the whole AG, and in these AB is equal to AC, the remainder BF is equal to the remainder CG. But FC was also proved equal to GB; therefore the two sides BF, FC are equal to the two sides CG, GB respectively; and the angle BFC is equal to the angle CGB, while the base BC is common to them; therefore the triangle BFC is also equal to the triangle CGB, and the remaining angles will be equal to the remaining angles respectively, namely those which the equal sides subtend; therefore the angle FBC is equal to the angle GCB, and the angle BCF to the angle

14

CBG. Accordingly, since the whole angle ABG was proved equal to the angle ACF, and in these the angle CBG is equal to the angle BCF, the remaining angle ABC is equal to the remaining angle ACB; and they are at the base of the triangle ABC. But the angle FBC was also proved equal to the angle GCB, and they are under the base. (Being) what it was required to prove."

The proof of this proposition is very probably Euclid's own. The reason for this conclusion is that Aristotle mentions the proof of this proposition and it is quite different from Euclid's. Hence, Aristotle must be quoting from the predecessors of Euclid. A paraphrase of the passage (Anal. Prior., I, 24, 41 b 13–22) runs as follows:

For let A, B be joined to the center. If, then, we assumed that the angle $E + C$ is equal to the angle $F + D$ without asserting

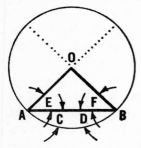

generally that the angles of semicircles are equal, and again that the angle C is equal to the angle D without making the further assumption that the two angles of all segments are equal, and if we then inferred, lastly, that, since the whole angles are equal, and equal angles are subtracted from them, the angles which remain, namely E, F, are equal, we should commit a petitio principii. (The fallacy of assuming what is to be proved.)

It seems quite certain that the only way that the mixed angles C and D could have been proved equal is by superposition. Euclid succeeded in this instance in avoiding a proof by superposition by changing the principle of the proof.

"Proposition 16. In any triangle, if one of the sides be produced, the exterior angle is greater than either of the interior and opposite angles.

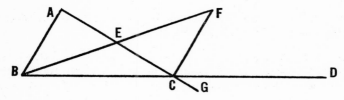

"Let ABC be a triangle, and let one side of it BC be produced to D; I say that the exterior angle ACD is greater than either of the interior and opposite angles CBA, BAC.

"Let AC be bisected at E (Prop. 10), and let BE be joined and produced in a straight line to F; let EF be made equal to BE (Prop. 3), let FC be joined (P. 1), and let AC be drawn through to G (P. 2). Then, since AE is equal to EC, and BE to EF, the two sides AE, EB are equal to the two sides CE, EF respectively; and the angle AEB is equal to the angle FEC, for they are vertical angles (Prop. 15). Therefore the base AB is equal to the base FC, and the triangle ABE is equal to the triangle CFE, and the remaining angles are equal to the remaining angles respectively, namely those which the equal sides subtend (Prop. 4); therefore the angle BAE is equal to the angle ECF. But the angle ECD is greater than the angle ECF (C.N. 5); therefore the angle ACD is greater than the angle BAE. Similarly also, if BC be bisected, the angle BCG, that is, the angle ACD (Prop. 15), can be proved greater than the angle ABC as well. Therefore, etc. (Being) what it was required to prove."

Euclid again appeals to his figure not for illustration but to collect a fact that he needs, namely that angle ECD is greater than angle ECF. The reason he assigns, C.N. 5, merely states that a whole is greater than a part, but does not prove that the angles in question have the relation of whole to part. That fact comes from the figure.

It is also interesting to note that he does not complete his proof in detail. He has not shown that the exterior angle at C is also greater than the angle ABC, except to indicate how that can be done. So even Euclid approved the pedagogical device, so annoying to students not overly interested in their subject, of compelling them to complete a proof. Would you like to finish Euclid's proof of this proposition?

"*Proposition 17. In any triangle two angles taken together in any manner are less than two right angles.*

"Let ABC be a triangle; I say that two angles of the triangle ABC taken together in any manner are less than two right angles.

"For let BC be produced to D (P. 2). Then, since the angle

16

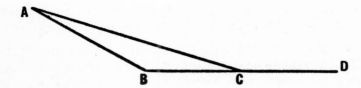

ACD is an exterior angle of the triangle ABC, it is greater than the interior and opposite angle ABC. Let angle ACB be added to each; therefore the angles ACD, ACB are greater than the angles ABC, BCA. But the angles ACD, ACB are equal to two right angles (Prop. 13). Therefore the angles ABC, BCA are less than two right angles. Similarly we can prove that the angles BAC, ACB are also less than two right angles, and so are the angles CAB, ABC as well. Therefore, etc. $Q.E.D.$"

What makes this proposition particularly interesting is the fact that it states the converse of the fifth postulate. It may explain why so many mathematicians attempted to prove that postulate as a proposition. Their efforts were vain, as we shall see, but led to the discovery of non-Euclidean geometry.

"*Proposition 27. If a straight line falling on two straight lines make the alternate angles equal to one another, the straight lines will be parallel to one another.*

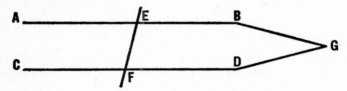

"For let the straight line EF falling on the two straight lines AB, CD make the alternate angles AEF, EFD equal to one another; I say that AB is parallel to CD.

"For, if not, AB, CD when produced will meet either in the direction of B, D or toward A, C. Let them be produced and meet, in the direction of B, D, at G. Then, in the triangle GEF, the exterior angle AEF is equal to the interior and opposite angle EFG; which is impossible (Prop. 16). Therefore AB, CD when produced will not meet in the direction of B, D. Similarly it can be proved that neither will they meet toward A, C. But straight

17

lines which do not meet in either direction are parallel; (Def. 23) therefore AB is parallel to CD. Therefore, etc. Q.E.D."

"**Proposition 28.** *If a straight line falling on two straight lines makes the exterior angle equal to the interior and opposite angle on the same side, or the interior angles on the same side equal to two right angles, the straight lines will be parallel to one another.*

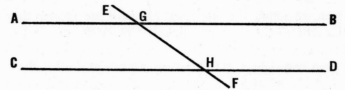

"For let the straight line EF falling on the two straight lines AB, DC make the exterior angle EGB equal to the interior and opposite angle GHD, or the interior angles on the same side, namely BGH, GHD, equal to two right angles; I say that AB is parallel to DC.

"For, since the angle EGB is equal to the angle GHD, while the angle EGB is equal to the angle AGH, the angle AGH is also equal to the angle GHD; and they are alternate; therefore AB is parallel to CD (Prop. 27). Again, since the angles BGH, GHD are equal to two right angles, and the angles AGH, BGH are also equal to two right angles (Prop. 13) the angles AGH, BGH are equal to the angles BGH, GHD. Let the angle BGH be subtracted from each; therefore the remaining angle AGH is equal to the remaining angle GHD; and they are alternate; therefore AB is parallel to CD (Prop. 27). Therefore, etc. Q.E.D."

"**Proposition 29.** *A straight line falling on parallel straight lines makes the alternate angles equal to one another, the exterior angle equal to the interior and opposite angle, and the interior angles on the same side equal to two right angles.*

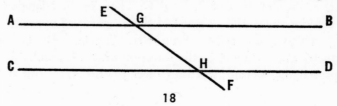

18

"For let the straight line EF fall on the parallel straight lines AB, DC; I say that it makes the alternate angles AGH, GHD equal, the exterior angle EGB equal to the interior and opposite angle GHD, and the interior angles on the same side, namely BGH, GHD, equal to two right angles.

"For, if the angle AGH is unequal to the angle GHD, one of them is greater. Let the angle AGH be greater. Let the angle BGH be added to each; therefore the angles AGH, BGH are greater than the angles BGH, GHD. But the angles AGH, BGH are equal to two right angles (Prop. 13); therefore the angles BGH, GHD are less than two right angles. But straight lines produced indefinitely from angles less than two right angles meet (P. 5); therefore AB, CD, if produced indefinitely, will meet; but they do not meet, because they are by hypothesis parallel. Therefore the angle AGH is not unequal to the angle GHD, and is therefore equal to it. Again, the angle AGH is equal to the angle EGB (Prop. 15); therefore the angle EGB is also equal to the angle GHD (C.N. 1). Let the angle BGH be added to each; therefore the angles EGB, BGH are equal to the angles BGH, GHD (C.N. 2). But the angles EGB, BGH are equal to two right angles (Prop. 13); therefore the angles BGH, GHD are also equal to two right angles. Therefore, etc. Q.E.D."

These three propositions, 27, 28, and 29 give us Euclid's theory of parallel lines. Proposition 29 is the converse of propositions 27 and 28. Euclid needs and uses his postulate 5 for the first time in proposition 29. This means that any geometry which shares Euclid's first four postulates, though it does not accept the fifth, will have all of Euclid's propositions 1 through 28 in common with his geometry.

We have given these three propositions because the first published book on non-Euclidean geometry had the title *The Theory of Parallels* and gave a theory different from the Euclidean theory.

19

CHAPTER II

Non-Euclidean Geometry

Anyone familiar with Euclidean geometry will find the concept of another geometry different from that of Euclid and contradicting the vast majority of the theorems of Euclid difficult to accept. This difficulty does not mark him as singular, for the admission of these geometries as an integral part of mathematics required the efforts of many mathematicians and centuries of time. But that acceptance has been accomplished and these geometries now share equally pride of place with Euclidean geometry. A good approach to this difficult subject is that of history. We shall therefore attempt to indicate in broad outline the history of the discovery of non-Euclidean geometry, and then explain briefly something of its nature.

The first mathematician who can be said to have contributed to the discovery of non-Euclidean geometry is, oddly enough, Euclid himself. Before the days of Euclid, the theory of parallel lines seems to have been defective. We gather as much from a criticism of Aristotle. Just what the defects were is not clear. To put the theory on a firm foundation Euclid formulated his fifth postulate: "That, if a straight line falling on two straight lines make the interior angles on the same side less than two right angles, the two straight lines, if produced indefinitely, meet on that side on which are the angles less than two right angles." This postulate put the theory of parallel lines on a firm foundation. However, it created a new problem. The postulate is not, like the other postulates, a brief and succinct statement of what everyone must admit. It is, moreover, the converse of proposition

17 of book one of Euclid's *Elements*. One would, therefore, expect that it ought to take its place as a proposition rather than as a postulate. Euclid himself apparently did not like his own postulate since he uses it as late and as little as possible. It appears for the first time in the proof of proposition 29 of book one. The abortive attempts of succeeding generations of mathematicians to prove Euclid's fifth postulate led finally to the discovery of non-Euclidean geometries. Hence Euclid must receive some of the credit for the discovery of these geometries.

One of the first attempts to prove Euclid's fifth postulate was made by the first *Ptolemy*. It was his interest in geometry which prompted him to invite Euclid to Alexandria to open a school there. The book he wrote on the subject has not come down to us, but it can be reconstructed in substance from what Proclus tells us about it. Ptolemy assumed, probably implicitly, that through a point not on a line one and only one parallel to the given line can be drawn. It is not difficult to show that this assumption is equivalent to the fifth postulate, for the postulate was introduced precisely to prove the proposition that only one line parallel to a given line can be drawn through a given point. Thus began a long series of proofs of the fifth postulate, all of them destined to prove failures.

Possidonius (first century B.C.) changed Euclid's definition of parallels and so made the fifth postulate unnecessary. In modern terminology he would say that two straight lines are parallel if everywhere equidistant. This definition, however, is open to very serious logical objections. It assigns two properties to lines which might well be inconsistent, that of being straight and of being equidistant. Thus to define a curve as an ellipse which is everywhere equidistant from a second ellipse is a definition in the same category as the definition of a square circle. The two properties of being an ellipse and of being everywhere equidistant from a second ellipse are contradictory properties. They are inconsistent. To prove that the properties of being a straight line and of being everywhere equidistant from another straight line are consistent Euclid's fifth postulate or its equivalent must be used.

Proclus (A.D. 410–485), a diligent commentator on geometry

21

and on the *Elements* of Euclid in particular, also attempted a proof of the fifth postulate. His proof consisted in trying to show that if a line cuts one of two parallel lines, it must cut the other also. The defect in his argument is that he assumes either that parallels are everywhere equidistant or that a perpendicular from a point on one of two parallel lines to the other always remains finite. Either hypothesis can be shown to be equivalent to the fifth postulate.

A very simple and brief proof which we reproduce in substance was given by *John Wallis* (1616–1703). He assumed explicitly the existence of similar triangles, that is triangles whose sides are equal and whose sides are proportional. Here is the proof:

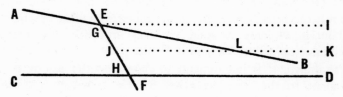

Let EF cut the lines AB and CD making the sum of the interior angles on the right less than two right angles; to show that AB and CD will meet if sufficiently produced.

Angle FGB and angle EGB together are equal to two right angles. But angle FGB and angle EHD together are less than two right angles. Therefore angle EGB is greater than angle EHD. Then if the segment HG is moved along EF with HD rigidly attached to it, until H coincides with G, then HD will have assumed the position GI and will lie entirely above GB. Hence, during its motion, HD must at some time cut GB, as, for example, when it coincides with JK, cutting GB at L. Now if one constructs a triangle on the base GH similar to the triangle GLJ — and this has been assumed to be possible — it is evident that HD must meet GB.

This proof is conclusive. However, the assumption made is equivalent to the fifth postulate, and hence it has not been shown that the fifth postulate is a necessary consequence of the other postulates.

We could list many other attempted direct proofs of the fifth postulate. All of them assumed in some form or other what had to be shown. Hence they all failed. We know now that all of them had to fail, for the fifth postulate is independent of the other postulates.

An Italian Jesuit, Gerolamo Saccheri (1667–1733), who taught logic and mathematics at Milan, was the first, as far as it is known, to attempt an indirect proof. He had already written a rather modern text on logic in which he made much of the argument *reductio ad absurdum*. In this type of argument one assumes the contradictory of the proposition that one wishes to prove, and then shows that this assumption leads to a contradiction. He now wrote a book on Euclid's fifth postulate *Euclides ab omni naevo vindicatus*. This book was rediscovered in 1889 and the first and most important part of the book republished in both English and Latin in 1920 (Halsted, Gerolamo Saccheri's *Euclides Vindicatus*, Chicago). Saccheri began with an isosceles quadrilateral* whose base angles are right angles. He easily proved that the remaining angles must be equal. If Euclid's fifth postulate is assumed, these angles must also be right angles. Hence Saccheri made two hypotheses: (a) that they are obtuse angles; (b) that they are acute angles. He expected that each of these hypotheses would lead to a contradiction, and if they did, he would have proved the fifth postulate. He had little trouble in finding a contradiction as the result of his first hypothesis. However, he would have found none if he had not assumed tacitly with Euclid that straight lines are not only boundless but infinite. His second hypothesis caused him much more trouble. He proved theorem after theorem, many of them classical theorems in what is now known as hyperbolic geometry, but the expected contradiction did not come. The best that he could do was to conclude rather lamely that in the hypothesis of the acute angle, two parallel lines would eventually meet at infinity and there have a common perpendicular. Not a very convincing contradiction since infinity had to enter the picture. The mathematician Harold Wolfe, in his book *Introduction to Non-Euclidean Geometry*, has this to say of Saccheri:

---

* Any rectangular figure is an isoceles bi-rectangular quadrilateral. Cf. p. 27 ff. *infra*.

23

Had Saccheri suspected that he had reached no contradiction simply because there was none to be reached, the discovery of Non-Euclidean geometry would have been made almost a century earlier than it was. Nevertheless, his is really a remarkable work. If the weak ending is ignored, together with a few other defects, the remainder marks Saccheri as a man who possessed geometric skill and logical penetration of high order. It was he who first had a glimpse of the three geometries, though he did not know it. He has been aptly compared with his fellow-countryman, Columbus, who went forth to discover a new route to a known land, but ended by discovering a new world.

Adrien Marie Legendre (1752–1833) also attempted to prove the fifth postulate indirectly. He attacked the problem by considering the sum of the angles of a triangle. In Euclid's geometry that sum is known to be exactly two right angles. Legendre assumed that it was greater than two right angles. He easily showed that this assumption is false, but had to assume the infinitude of the line in his proof. It is an interesting proof and may be summarized as follows:

Assume the sum of the angles of triangle ABC to be $180° + \theta$ and that angle CAB is not greater than either of the others. Let D be the mid-point of BC and through A and D draw AE making $DE = AD$. Then triangles ABD and ECD are congruent

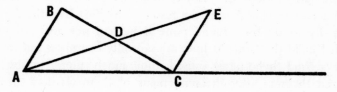

since two sides and the included angle of one are equal respectively to two sides and the included angle of the other (Euclid I, 4). Also the sum of the angles of triangle AEC is also $180° + \theta$, since angles EAC and AEC equal angle A of triangle ABC, while angle ACE is equal to the sum of the angles C and B of triangle ABC. In triangle EAC one of the angles AEC or EAC is less than or equal to ½ angle BAC, for their sum is angle BAC. If we repeat the construction for the triangle AEC, we shall have a new triangle in which one of the angles is less than ¼ the angle BAC while the sum of the angles of the triangle is still equal to $180° + \theta$. Repeat the construction n times, and this is possible if we assume that all lines are infinite. We finally have a triangle in which the sum of the angles is $180° + \theta$, and in which one angle is less than $(½)^n$ of angle BAC. By the Archimedean hypothesis we can choose n so large that $(½)^n$ of angle BAC is less than θ. But this gives us a contradiction, for we should then have a triangle in which the sum of two of the angles is greater than two right angles, contrary to Euclid I, 17.

Legendre made many attempts to prove that the assumption that the sum of the angles was less than two right angles was also false, but failed to find any contradiction.

The time was now ripe for the discovery of non-Euclidean geometry. As so often happens with regard to great discoveries, the discovery of the non-Euclidean geometry now known as hyperbolic geometry was made almost simultaneously but independently, in this case by three men: *Carl Friederich Gauss* (1777–1855), a German mathematician, justly conceded by his contemporaries to be the greatest mathematician of his time; *Johann Bolyai* (Bolyai Janos, 1802–1860), a Hungarian; and *Nikolai Ivanovich Lobachevsky* (1793–1856), a Russian. Of these three, Gauss published nothing on the subject, though it is certain from his letters that he knew this new geometry as the result of his own investigations. Lobachevsky published his results as early as 1829, but in Russian, and little attention was paid to his work. He then wrote articles about his discovery in German and French to publicize his work. His book *Geometrische Untersuchungen zur Theorie der Parallelinien* brought his work to the attention of Gauss and Bolyai. Bolyai published his findings as an appendix to his father's book *Tentamen Juventutem Studiosam in Elementa Matheseos Purae, Elementaris ac Sublimioris, Methodo Intuitiva Evidentique Huic Propria, Introducendi. Cum Appendice Triplici.* This was in 1832.

A translation of Lobachevsky's German work is available (Open Court Publishing Co., La Salle, Illinois, 1914), and makes instructive reading. Lobachevsky was dissatisfied with Euclid's theory of parallel lines. Euclid was able to prove that if a perpendicular AB is drawn to a line CD, and if through the point A a line is

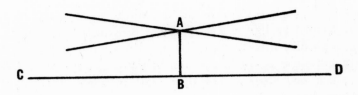

drawn perpendicular to AB, this line will not meet CD no matter how far produced. It verifies Euclid's definition of parallel lines. To prove that this is the only line that can be drawn parallel to CD, Euclid had to use his fifth postulate. Lobachevsky discarded the fifth postulate and considered all lines that could be drawn through the point A. These he divided into two classes, those which intersected CD and those which did not. He assumed that more than one line did not intersect CD. He was then able to prove that the set of lines that did intersect CD had no last member, but that the set that did not intersect CD had a first member. There were two such lines, one in either direction. These he termed parallel lines. The others of the same set he called nonintersecting lines. He then developed a long series of theorems all dependent on his original assumption which contradicted Euclid's fifth postulate. He argued that if his assumption was false, a contradiction must appear. But he found no contradiction and finally came to the conclusion that there never would be one. If that were the case, he had discovered a new geometry. The more he pondered the matter, the more convinced he became that this was actually the case, and he published his findings. We know today that his surmise was correct, and he is credited as one of the discoverers of non-Euclidean geometry. His geometry is now called hyperbolic geometry.

All the theorems of Euclidean geometry which do not involve Euclid's fifth postulate, hence all the propositions of Euclid's *Elements*, Book I, propositions 1–28, are valid in this new geometry. Some of the new theorems are the following: Two lines cannot be equidistant; a line may intersect one of two parallel lines without intersecting the other; similar triangles are necessarily congruent; three points may be neither collinear nor concyclic.

The next name of note in the field of non-Euclidean geometry

26

is that of *Georg Friederich Bernhard Riemann* (1826–1866). He was the first to suggest that an unbounded line need not necessarily be infinite. This suggestion led to a second type of non-Euclidean geometry in which all lines are finite. In this geometry there are no parallel lines, for all lines intersect. The sum of the angles of a triangle in this geometry is always greater than 180°. This geometry is now known as elliptic geometry.

A final name must be added to our list of the pioneers who made substantial contributions to non-Euclidean geometry, namely that of *Eugenio Beltrami* (1835–1900), an Italian. He was born at Cremona, and became a professor at Bologna. To him belongs the credit of having given the first proof of the consistency of the non-Euclidean geometries in 1868. He showed that these geometries could be represented, with restrictions, on a Euclidean surface of constant curvature. Consequently any inconsistency in one of the non-Euclidean geometries would imply an inconsistency in Euclid's geometry. His discovery placed non-Euclidean geometries on as firm a foundation as that of Euclidean geometry.

To remove some of the mystery which shrouds non-Euclidean geometry, we shall examine some of the theorems of these geometries. An excellent introduction is the book of Father Saccheri, who, as we have seen, was the first mathematician to view many of the theorems of these geometries, though he did not realize that they were theorems of new geometries. We shall reproduce a number of his theorems. Our presentation will not be a translation but an adaptation.

The first two theorems are true in both Euclidean and non-Euclidean geometries. They are necessary foundations for his non-Euclidean theorems.

Theorem 1. In an isosceles quadrilateral ABCD, the angles at C and D are equal.

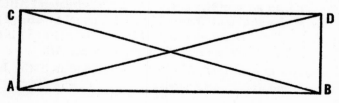

Proof: Let ABCD be an isosceles quadrilateral with CA equal to DB, and the angles at A and B equal. Draw AD and BC. In the triangles ABD and BAC, the angles at A and B are given equal. AB is a common side, and AC is given equal to BD. Therefore the triangles are congruent by Euclid I, 4. Therefore AD is equal to CB.

Now consider the triangles ACD and BCD. In these triangles the three sides are respectively equal. Hence by Euclid I, 8 corresponding angles are equal. Hence angle C is equal to angle D.

Theorem 2. In an isosceles quadrilateral ABCD let M be the mid-point of AB and H the mid-point of CD, then HM is perpendicular to both AB and CD.

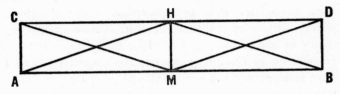

Proof: Join AH, BH, CM, and DM. In the triangles CAM and DBM, CM = DM by Euclid I, 4. Similarly in triangles ACH and BDH, AH = BH. Therefore in the triangles CHM and DHM the angles at H are equal by Euclid I, 8. Hence they are right angles. Similarly, the angles at M are equal, from a consideration of the triangles HAM and HBM.

It is to be noted that Saccheri may appeal to any of the first twenty-eight theorems of Euclid, Book One, since none of these theorems depend on the fifth postulate.

The following theorem is the first non-Euclidean theorem. It gives a fundamental property of an isosceles bi-rectangular quadrilateral in each of the three geometries, Euclidean geometry, elliptic geometry, hyperbolic geometry.

Theorem 3. In an isosceles bi-rectangular quadrilateral ABCD, (1) if the angles at C and D are right, CD is equal to AB; (2) if the angles at C and D are obtuse, CD is less than AB; (3) if the angles at C and D are acute, CD is greater than AB.

An isosceles quadrilateral ABCD is bi-rectangular if the base angles at A and B are right angles.

28

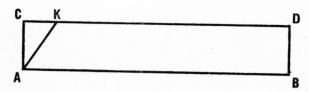

Proof of (1): If CD is not equal to AB, one is larger than the other. Let it be CD. Choose K so that DK is equal to AB, and draw KA. Since KD and AB are perpendicular to DB, the angles DKA and BAK are equal (Theorem 1). But this is absurd since the angle BAK is by construction less than the given angle BAC; and the angle DKA is by construction external and therefore greater than the internal opposite angle DCA (Euclid I, 16) which is given right.

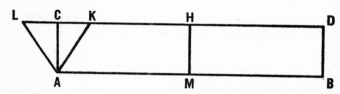

Proof of (2): Bisect CD at H and AB at M and join HM. Since AM and CH are perpendicular to HM by Theorem 2, and since A is a right angle and C is obtuse, CH is not equal to AM by Theorem 1. Neither is CH greater than AM; for if CH is greater, assume the piece KH in HC equal to AM and draw KA. Then the angles at A and K will be equal by Theorem 1, which is absurd as above in the proof of (1). Therefore CH is less than AM. Hence since $2CH = CD$ and $2AM = AB$, CD is less than AB.

Proof of (3): CH is not equal to AM since CH and AM are perpendicular to HM and the angle at A is right while the angle at C is acute (Theorem 1). Neither is CH less than AM. If it were, we could produce CH to L so that HL equals AM, and join LA. Then the angles at L and A will be equal (Theorem 1). But this is absurd for angle MAL is greater than a right angle and angle ALC is less than the exterior acute angle at C (Euclid I, 16). Therefore CH is greater than AM, and hence DC is greater than AB.

29

Theorem 4. In an isosceles bi-rectangular quadrilateral ABCD, (1) if CD equals AB, the angles at C and D are right; (2) if CD is less than AB, the angles at C and D are obtuse; (3) if CD is greater than AB, the angles at C and D are acute.

Proof: This is the converse of theorem 3 and a necessary corollary of that theorem.

Definitions. Since the straight line joining the extremities of equal perpendiculars, standing upon the same straight line which we call base, makes equal angles with these perpendiculars, therefore there are three hypotheses to be distinguished according to the species of these angles. The first we shall call the *hypothesis of the right angle* [Euclidean geometry]; the second the *hypothesis of the obtuse angle* [Elliptic geometry]; and the third the *hypothesis of the acute angle* [Hyperbolic geometry].

In theorems 5, 6, and 7, Saccheri proves that these three hypotheses are mutually exclusive. If one is verified even in a single instance, then it alone is true and the others are false.

Theorem 8. Given any triangle ABD, right-angled at B; prolong DA to any point X, and through A erect HAC perpendicular to AB, the point H being within the angle XAB. Then angle XAH will be equal to, or less, or greater than the internal and opposite angle ADB, according as the hypothesis of the right angle, or of the obtuse angle, or of the acute angle is true, and conversely.

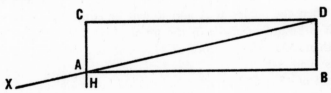

Proof: Assume in *HC* the portion *AC* equal to *BD*, and join *CD*. *CD* will be, in the hypothesis of the right angle, equal to *AB* (Theorem 3). Therefore the angle *ADB* will be equal to the angle *DAC* (Euclid I, 8), or to its equal the angle *XAH* (Euclid I, 15).

Then, in the hypothesis of the obtuse angle, *CD* will be less than *AB* (Theorem 3). Wherefore in the triangles *ADB*, *DAC*

30

the angle DAC, or its vertical XAH, will be less than the angle ADB (Euclid I, 25).

Finally, in the hypothesis of the acute angle, CD will be greater than the opposite AB (Theorem 3). Wherefore in the triangle DAC the angle DAC, or its vertical XAH, will be greater than the angle ADB.

Conversely: if the angle CAD, or its vertical XAH, is equal to the internal and opposite angle ADB, the join CD will be equal to AB (Euclid I, 4), and therefore the hypothesis of the right angle will be true (Theorem 4).

But if the angle CAD, or its vertical XAH, is less or greater than the internal or opposite ADB, also the join CD will be less or greater than AB (Euclid I, 24); and therefore the hypothesis of the obtuse angle or the hypothesis of the acute angle respectively will be true (Theorem 4).

Theorem 9. *In any right-angled triangle the two acute angles remaining are, taken together, equal to one right angle in the hypothesis of the right angle; greater than one right angle, in the hypothesis of the obtuse angle; but less than one right angle in the hypothesis of the acute angle.*

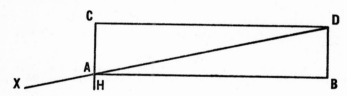

Proof: For if the angle XAH is equal to angle ADB, which is certain from the preceding proposition in the hypothesis of the right angle, then the angle ADB makes up with the angle HAD two right angles, as (Euclid I, 13) the aforesaid angle XAH makes them up with this angle HAD. Wherefore, the right angle HAB being subtracted, the two angles ADB and BAD remain together equal to one right angle.

However, if the angle XAH is less than the angle ADB, which is certain from the preceding proposition in the hypothesis of the obtuse angle, then the angle ADB makes up with the angle HAD more than two right angles, since with it (Euclid I, 13) the angle XAH makes up two. Wherefore, the angle HAB being subtracted, the two angles ADB and BAD will be together greater than one right angle.

Finally, if the angle XAH be greater than the angle ADB, which is certain from the preceding proposition in the hypothesis of the acute angle, then the angle ADB will make up less than two right angles with the angle HAD, since with this angle XAH makes up two. Wherefore, subtracting the right angle HAB, the angles ADB and BAD will be together less than one right angle.

A corollary of this theorem is that the sum of the angles in any triangle is exactly two right angles in the hypothesis of the right angle; is greater than two right angles in the hypothesis of the obtuse angle; is less than two right angles in the hypothesis of the acute angle. This follows since any triangle can be divided into two right triangles by dropping a perpendicular from the vertex of the largest angle to the opposite side.

CHAPTER III

The Problem of the Geometries

Many of the geometries discovered since Euclid's day posed no problems, for their theorems did not contradict any of the theorems of Euclidean geometry. Thus Descartes' discovery of analytic geometry, which is the application of algebra to geometry, opened up new horizons, facilitated the proofs of many Euclidean theorems, and led to the discovery of many additional theorems whose very existence had not even been suspected. The same was true of projective geometry introduced by Chasles and Steiner independently. Projective geometry studies those properties of geometric configurations which are unchanged when projected from one plane to another. Thus intersecting lines remain intersecting lines under projection so that linearity and intersection are projective properties. Since a circle does not always project into a circle but into an ellipse, the property of being circular is not a projective property. All these new geometries enriched the sum total of geometric theorems; none contradicted any previously established theorem.

The discovery of non-Euclidean geometry was different. Here were geometries many of whose theorems contradicted the theorems of Euclidean geometry. Little wonder then that they were not at once hailed with joy. Their discovery was embarrassing. What was to be done with these new geometries? What effect would they have on the old, traditional geometry? Since there were now contradictory geometries, which geometry was true? Men had always taken for granted that they lived in a Euclidean world. Was that belief still valid? If an answer could be found to this question, the problem of the geometries would be solved.

When we first begin to consider the problem as to which geometry applies to the world in which we live, the prospect of an easy solution is bright. After all, the geometries contain propositions which mutually contradict each other. Thus the sum of the angles of a triangle are equal to two right angles in Euclidean geometry, are less than two right angles in hyperbolic geometry, and are greater than two right angles in elliptic geometry. Hence the problem will be solved if we can determine just what the sum of the angles of a triangle is in the universe in which we live.

By way of illustration, let us assume that we do not know whether the earth is flat or spherical, and that we seek an answer based on geometry. We recall that in Euclidean spherical geometry the sum of the angles of any spherical triangle is always greater than two right angles, while in Euclidean plane geometry the sum of the angles of a plane triangle is always exactly two right angles. To solve our problem, then, we decide to measure the angles in a physical triangle. For our surface we might use a frozen lake. Three points on that surface might be connected by wires drawn taut to insure the shortest distance between points. The angles could then be measured. We should find, as we took larger and larger triangles, that the sum of the angles would finally become larger than two right angles by an amount greater than the calculated percentage of instrumental and observational error. We would then know that the earth is spherical, and that for large portions of the earth's surface we must use spherical geometry, but that for small portions plane geometry gives sufficiently accurate results.

It is worthy of note that our experiment would have failed if the earth were actually flat. The reason for the failure would be the fact that there is always an instrumental and observational error in all measurements. Better instruments and a better technique can reduce the size of this error but cannot eliminate it. Hence the experiment could not establish the fact that the earth is flat — if it actually were — since we could always suppose that it is a sphere of so large a radius that the difference between

34

its geometry and the geometry of a plane is covered by the observational error.

Now we are very much in the same position when we attempt to determine whether the geometry of the physical universe is Euclidean or non-Euclidean. It is difficult to find a suitably large physical triangle. Its sides would have to be rays of light joining distant stars with the earth. Such measurements up to the present have not resolved the problem. All that we can say is that Euclidean geometry gives sufficiently accurate results. However, whether the geometry of the universe is Euclidean or non-Euclidean we do not know. This much we can say. If the theory of relativity of Einstein gives an accurate picture of the physical universe, then the geometry of the universe is not Euclidean, because the geometry essential to Einstein's theory is non-Euclidean.

Philosophers, particularly scholastic philosophers, have attempted to prove that Euclidean geometry is the geometry of the universe on philosophical grounds. Fundamental to their argument is the process of abstraction. They reason that Euclidean geometry is achieved by abstraction from the physical universe, and since abstraction does not change the object on which it is exercised but merely considers some aspects of it to the neglect of others, the geometry of the universe is Euclidean. But suppose that the geometry of the universe actually is non-Euclidean, but differs from Euclidean by an amount too small to be detected by any means available to the philosopher. Would not the same process of abstraction reveal the geometry of the universe as Euclidean, when actually it is not?

If you insist with Father Peter Hoenen, S.J., professor of cosmology at the Gregorian University in Rome, that the geometry of extension is Euclidean whatever may be the geometry of the physical universe, it is difficult to see how you are asserting anything more than that Euclidean geometry is a valid geometry in the sense of a self-consistent science. But then so are the other geometries, one of which may actually be the geometry of the physical universe.

There have been and still are philosophers who advocate even more extreme views. Father J. M. Dario, S.J., published his

35

Praelectiones Cosmologiae in 1923. He insists that there is only one geometry, namely Euclidean geometry. For him the logical systems called non-Euclidean geometries are geometry only by an abuse of language. He asserts that in these geometries figures cannot be drawn; that those who study these geometries themselves admit that they do not apply to the universe in which we live. Evidently his sources of information about these geometries must have been very much secondhand and very much at fault. Yet his views still persist. One still meets too many philosophers who think as he does.

The problem of the geometries is also a mathematical problem, but not in the sense that the mathematician must determine which geometry applies to the universe. That is a problem for the physical scientist and/or philosopher. The mathematician's problem is to bring order into the mathematical universe threatened by the simultaneous presence of contradictory theorems. This was done by changing the foundations of the science. Formerly these foundations consisted of what were thought to be — and in some cases actually were — self-evident truths. The new foundations are not self-evident truths but pure postulates, that is, propositions which the mathematician agrees to accept in order to study the mathematics that they imply. These postulates should be at least approximations to the truth, the closer, the better, since mathematics is not a game for the amusement of the few — some mathematicians to the contrary notwithstanding — but a serious and difficult occupation which the modern world finds increasingly necessary, not to say useful, in conducting its practical affairs. Despite the change of the foundations, the purpose of the science remains unchanged. It is still to give as accurate a picture as possible of the mathematics of the universe. The fact that the mathematician can no longer say what the geometry of the universe truly is merely points up the limitations of human knowledge even in this advanced day and age.

If, with the mathematicians, you adopt this point of view, the problem of the geometries is solved. Each geometry is a logical deduction from a set of postulates, and all geometries are on an equal footing. The mathematician now is not concerned with the problem as to which geometry applies to the world in which we live. He leaves that problem for others to solve. However, he has simplified the problem. It is not necessary to consider all the propositions of any geometry to determine whether or not it applies in a given setting. It is sufficient merely to examine the postulates. If they give a sufficiently close approximation, then so will all the theorems derived from them.

It might be well to conclude this brief chapter with some general remarks about the geometries. Though the terms points, lines, and planes are used in all the geometries, they do not represent the same objects in each despite the fact that they have the same name. Thus, a Euclidean line is not the same as a line in either hyperbolic or elliptic geometry. The same holds for planes. For these objects, though undefined, have the properties assigned to them by the postulates. But the postulates differ; therefore, so do the lines and planes. If this is borne in mind, much of the mystery that shrouds non-Euclidean geometries will be dissipated.

CHAPTER IV

What Is Mathematics?

We have already indicated in the last chapter that the discovery of non-Euclidean geometry led to a change in the foundations of mathematics; instead of beginning with self-evident truths a mathematical science now begins with pure postulates. Just what this means and implies we shall attempt to explain in the present chapter.

In every science we find a number of terms. In order that we may know what they mean in a particular science, the terms must be defined. Complex terms are defined in terms of the less complex. Evidently this process of definition cannot be continued indefinitely. Eventually we must arrive at terms which cannot be further simplified. These terms are left undefined and are called *undefined terms*. And these words mean exactly what they say. No descriptive definition may be attempted of the undefined terms, because such descriptions might be the occasion for the exercise of intuition in the proofs of some propositions and the unconscious introduction of properties which are not listed in the postulates. Such proofs, of course, would be invalid. To make sure that no foreign properties are introduced, mathematicians frequently use symbols for the undefined terms, symbols which, as far as that is possible, are devoid of meaning.

In every deductive science there are many propositions. Among them there is a certain hierarchy. One proposition follows from one or more other propositions. To establish such a relationship is to prove a proposition. Obviously again, not all the propositions of a given science can be proved in this technical sense. We must come to propositions which are incapable of proof. Such propositions are called *postulates*. Their function is to list those properties of the undefined terms which are to be used in the given science. They must, of course, list all of them. Once the postulates have been determined upon or selected, no other unproved propositions are to be admitted to the science. These unproved propositions are not self-evident truths for the simple reason that a proposition assigning properties to undefined terms cannot possibly be either true or false, since a proposition is true or false only in so far as it affirms or denies a real property of a real object.

The postulates, then, are statements of properties which we agree the undefined terms shall possess. Three properties are predicated of the postulates. They must be *consistent*, should be *independent*, and may be *categorical*. We say that a set of postulates is *consistent* if it is impossible to deduce from the given postulates both a proposition and its contradictory. This property of a set of postulates is obviously not only desirable but essential. Without it no science is possible. The set of postulates is said to be *independent* if no single postulate of the set is a consequence of any or all of the others. Independence is not essential but highly desirable. It assures a clear-cut distinction between the postulates and the propositions, for any so-called postulate which is a consequence of other postulates is by that very fact not a postulate but a proposition. The postulates are said to be *categorical* if they apply essentially to only one set of objects, or, if to several sets, then these sets are isomorphic, i.e., not essentially different. This property of the postulates is not always necessary or even desirable, since it limits the application of the science. Yet, if the science is to give a complete and unique characterization of any set of objects, then the postulates of that science must be categorical.

We shall illustrate with a miniature mathematical science. It appeared in mathematical literature for the first time in the two-volume work *Projective Geometry* by Veblen and Young published in 1910.

The undefined terms:
1. A class S of elements $A, B, C, \ldots$
2. m-class.
3. The relation: an element belongs to a class.

The postulates:
1. If A and B are distinct elements of S, there is at least one m-class containing both A and B.
2. If A and B are distinct elements of S, there is not more than one m-class containing both A and B.
3. Any two m-classes have at least one element in common.
4. There exists at least one m-class.
5. Every m-class contains at least three elements of S.
6. All the elements of S do not belong to the same m-class.
7. No m-class contains more than three elements of S.

Note that our undefined terms are really undefined. Note, too, that we use letters of the alphabet to symbolize our elements. We use them as mere symbols.

Our first question concerning the postulates is: Are they logically consistent? We cannot answer this question by saying that the set enunciates only self-evident truths and hence is of necessity consistent. In fact no single assumption can be said to be either true or false since the terms that they contain, elements of S and m-class, are undefined and are devoid of meaning. To prove the consistency of this set, we exhibit a concrete representation of our assumptions by interpreting the class S to mean the digits 1, 2, ..., 7, and the m-classes to mean the columns in the following table.

$$(1) \quad \begin{array}{ccccccc}
1 & 2 & 3 & 4 & 5 & 6 & 7 \\
2 & 3 & 4 & 5 & 6 & 7 & 1 \\
4 & 5 & 6 & 7 & 1 & 2 & 3
\end{array}$$

All our assumptions are true of this set of number triples as can easily be verified. Thus 5 and 7 are two distinct elements of S. By postulate 1 there is an m-class containing both 5 and 7. Here it is the fourth column. By postulate 2, there is not more than one m-class containing both 5 and 7. As we see there is no other column containing both 5 and 7. We can verify the truth

40

of the first two postulates for the remaining twenty combinations of two numbers chosen from the elements of S. To verify the third postulate, we must make sure that every column has at least one number in common with every other. Thus the first column has 2 in common with the second column, 4 in common with the third, 4 in common with the fourth, 1 in common with the fifth, 2 with the sixth, and finally 1 in common with the seventh. We do the same with the other columns. The remaining postulates are obviously true of our model. Therefore every proposition which we can logically derive from our assumptions must be true of this set of triples. Hence none of the assumptions can be inconsistent with the rest; otherwise contradictory statements would be true of this system of triples, and that is impossible.

We are now in a position to derive a number of theorems from our postulates. By means of these theorems we shall be able to show that our set of postulates is also independent and categorical.

Theorem 1. Any two distinct elements of S determine one and only one m-class containing both these elements.

Proof: Let A and B be two distinct elements of S. Then by postulate 1 there is an m-class containing both A and B, and by postulate 2 there is only one such m-class.

Theorem 2. Any two m-classes have one and only one element of S in common.

Proof: Any two m-classes have at least one element in common by postulate 3. They cannot have two elements in common by theorem 1, according to which any two distinct elements determine a unique m-class.

Theorem 3. There exists three elements of S which are not all in the same m-class.

Proof: There exists at least one m-class (P. 4). This m-class contains at least three elements (P. 5). Not all the elements of S belong to the same m-class (P. 6). Hence in addition to the three elements we already have, there exists at least one other element. If we choose this element together with two of the three

41

in the given m-class, we have three elements not all of which belong to the same m-class.

Theorem 4. Any class S subject to assumptions one to six inclusively contains at least seven elements.

Proof: There are three distinct elements of S not all in the same m-class (T. 3). Let them be A, B, C. Then AB, BC, AC determine distinct m-classes (T. 1). Each of these m-classes requires a third element to complete it (P. 5). These new elements must be distinct from each other and from A, B, C (P. 2). Let them be D, E, G. Then we have the four m-classes ABD, BCE, ACG, and DEG. In addition we have the incomplete m-classes DC, EA, GB (P. 1), and these require a third element to complete them (P. 5). This new element must be distinct from those we already have (P. 2). Let it be F. We now have seven elements arranged in seven m-classes according to the following table, where the columns are the m-classes.

$$
(2) \quad
\begin{array}{ccccccc}
A & B & C & D & E & F & G \\
B & C & D & E & F & G & A \\
D & E & F & G & A & B & C
\end{array}
$$

We note in passing that this table differs from the previous table (1) in this only, that the numbers 1, 2, 3, ..., 7 have been replaced by the letters A, B, ..., G.

Theorem 5. Any class S subject to assumptions one to seven contains only seven elements.

Proof: The proof will consist in showing that it is impossible to add another element T to the set S which we have already arranged into m-classes as in table (2). Since T and A are distinct elements they determine an m-class by postulate one, and by postulate three this m-class TA must have an element in common with the m-class BFG. This element cannot be B, for then BTA and BTAD would belong to the same m-class contrary to postulate seven. It cannot be F, for then TAF and ETAF would belong to the same m-class also contrary to postulate seven. It cannot be G, for then TAG and TAGC would belong to the same m-class contrary to postulate seven. Hence the existence of T implies the existence of four elements in the m-class BFG which is likewise contrary to postulate seven.

We are now in a position to analyze our set of assumptions. These assumptions or postulates are categorical, that is to say there is essentially only one class S of elements which satisfy them, for theorems 4 and 5 show that every class S of elements must contain seven and only seven elements distributed into m-classes as indicated by table (2). Hence if there are two classes S and S' of seven elements each, we can set up a one-to-one correspondence between the elements of these classes which preserves subdivision into m-classes. Thus, if we have two classes of elements $A, B, \ldots, G$ and $A', B', \ldots, G'$, and if A corresponds to A' and B to B', then the m-class AB must correspond to the m-class $A'B'$. In other words if C is the third element in AB and C' the third element in $A'B'$, then C must correspond to C'. We then say that the two classes S and S' are simply *isomorphic*. They have the same mathematical structure. Mathematically they are indistinguishable. Thus the set

$$\begin{array}{ccccccc} A' & B' & D' & C' & E' & F' & G' \\ B' & D' & C' & E' & F' & G' & A' \\ C' & E' & F' & G' & A' & B' & D' \end{array}$$

is isomorphic with the set (2). The one-to-one correspondence in this case is

$$\begin{array}{ccccccc} A & B & C & D & E & F & G \\ A' & B' & D' & C' & E' & F' & G' \end{array}$$

where letters in the same column correspond to each other.

If we omit from our set of postulates the last one, the remaining postulates are no longer categorical. We prove this statement by exhibiting a new class S consisting of the digits $1, 2, \ldots, 13$ arranged into m-classes of four elements each according to the following table.

$$(3) \quad \begin{array}{ccccccccccccc} 1 & 2 & 3 & 4 & 5 & 6 & 7 & 8 & 9 & 10 & 11 & 12 & 13 \\ 2 & 3 & 4 & 5 & 6 & 7 & 8 & 9 & 10 & 11 & 12 & 13 & 1 \\ 4 & 5 & 6 & 7 & 8 & 9 & 10 & 11 & 12 & 13 & 1 & 2 & 3 \\ 10 & 11 & 12 & 13 & 1 & 2 & 3 & 4 & 5 & 6 & 7 & 8 & 9 \end{array}$$

It is not difficult though certainly tedious to verify postulates one

43

to six of this new class of thirteen elements. Obviously, it is impossible to set up a one-to-one correspondence between these thirteen elements and the original seven. It follows therefore that the first six postulates are not categorical since they are verified of at least two classes of elements which are not simply isomorphic.

Table (3) also establishes the fact that postulate seven is independent of the other six postulates, that is to say, postulate seven cannot be derived from the other six because these six can all be true of a system in which postulate seven is false.

But each of the other postulates is also independent, and we shall now prove that this is indeed the case. To prove the independence of postulate one, we use the set S of elements 1, 2, ..., 5. Let there be two m-classes, 1,2,3 and 3,4,5. Then all the postulates except the first are satisfied in this set. Hence postulate one is independent of the other six.

If set S consists of the elements 1, 2, 3, 4, and the m-classes are the columns in the table

$$\begin{array}{ccc} 1 & 1 & 3 \\ 2 & 2 & 4 \\ 3 & 4 & 1 \end{array}$$

then all the postulates except two are verified. Hence, postulate two is independent of the rest, since all can be true of a set in which two is false.

To prove the independence of postulate three a set S of the elements 1, 2, ..., 9 arranged into m-classes according to the following table may be used.

$$\begin{array}{cccccccccccc} 1 & 4 & 1 & 1 & 1 & 2 & 2 & 2 & 3 & 3 & 3 & 7 \\ 2 & 5 & 4 & 5 & 6 & 4 & 5 & 6 & 4 & 5 & 6 & 8 \\ 3 & 6 & 7 & 8 & 9 & 9 & 7 & 8 & 8 & 9 & 7 & 9 \end{array}$$

In this table the first two m-classes have no element in common. Hence postulate three is false of this set. All the others are true.

Postulate four is a postulate which any nonmathematician must find, to say the least, unusual. It postulates existence. For a nonmathematician existence is something which is verified, not postulated. Existence by legislation is certainly something not found in Euclid. However, it is a consequence of the mathema-

44

tician's new approach. He begins with undefined terms which are to have no properties except those assigned to them by the postulates. Existence is a property, and so logically there should be a postulate listing that property.

To prove the independence of postulate four, symbolic logic rather than Aristotelian logic is necessary. Both, of course, are valid systems of logic. The difference between them, as far as we are concerned at present, is a difference in the interpretation of the word "all." In mathematical logic "all" means "without exception." In Aristotelian logic "all" means not only "without exception" but also that there exists at least one element in the set. Thus, if a mathematician makes the statement "All the marbles in this bag are white," he means that there are no marbles of any other color in the bag. He does not mean to say that there are any marbles in the bag. If he does mean also that the bag is not empty, he must state so explicitly. For Aristotle, on the other hand, the statement "All the marbles in this bag are white" means two things. It means both that there are marbles in the bag and that all of them are white. If we bear this distinction in mind, we can prove the independence of postulate four. Let S be a class which contains no elements. Such classes are called null classes. Then all the postulates except four are true of this set S which contains no elements. For example, the first postulate, which states that if A and B are two distinct elements of S, then there is one m-class containing A and B, is true. Those who recognize no logic except that of Aristotle cannot prove the independence of postulate four except on the metaphysical ground that existence for any created object, even undefined m-classes, is always contingent. It never follows as a consequence of any other property. That such an argument should not appeal to a mathematician when a mathematical argument is available is but natural.

We prove the independence of the fifth postulate with a set S of elements 1, 2, 3, where the m-classes are the pairs 1 2, 2 3, 1 3. Then all the postulates except five are satisfied.

Finally if S is the set 1, 2, 3 and if there is only one m-class which contains all three elements, then all the postulates except six are verified.

Since our miniature mathematical science was merely an artificial illustration of modern mathematics, the reader may ask just how closely this model science approximates modern mathematics. We shall answer this question by giving a very brief introduction to the theory of finite groups, an important contribution to mathematics made at the end of the nineteenth and the beginning of the twentieth centuries.

INTRODUCTION TO THE THEORY OF GROUPS

The undefined terms
1. A class G of undefined elements $A, B, C, \ldots$
2. An undefined operation, which we shall call multiplication, and denote by the symbol $\circ$.

The postulates
1. If A and B are any two elements of G, then $A \circ B = C$ is an element of G.
2. For any three elements A, B, C of G, we have $A \circ (B \circ C) = (A \circ B) \circ C$.
3. There exists an element E of G such that for all A of G $E \circ A = A$.
4. For all A of G there exists an inverse element A^{-1} such that $A^{-1} \circ A = E$.

Note that we do not assume the commutative law, $A \circ B = B \circ A$. If this law is satisfied by the group elements, the group is said to be Abelian after the Norwegian mathematician Niels H. Abel (1802–1829).

We prove the consistency of the group postulates by giving examples of groups. Thus the positive and negative integers and zero form a group under addition. The set of all rational numbers exclusive of zero form a group if the group operation is multiplication.

Another group of a different kind is the set of those rotations of a hexagon about its center which bring its vertices into coincidence. These rotations are $A = 60° + n.360°$ for all integral n, since all such rotations bring vertex 1 into the position originally occupied by vertex 2. $B = 120° + n.360°$, $C = 180° + n.360°$,

46

$D = 240° + n.360°$, $F = 300° + n.360°$,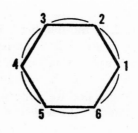
$E = 0° + n.360°$. This last rotation is
the unit rotation or the unit element in
the group since it leaves the position of
each vertex of the hexagon unchanged.
Here the group operation merely means
the successive performance of the indicated rotations. Thus $A \circ B = C$ since
a rotation through 60° followed by a rotation through 120° is the
same as a rotation through 180°. To study this group more
conveniently, we shall construct its multiplication table. This
is a table which exhibits all possible products of the elements
of our group.

(4)

	E	A	B	C	D	F
E	E	A	B	C	D	F
A	A	B	C	D	F	E
B	B	C	D	F	E	A
C	C	D	F	E	A	B
D	D	F	E	A	B	C
F	F	E	A	B	C	D

The first line and the first column of this table list all the elements
of the group. To find any product from the group table, find the
first element of the product in the first column on the left, the
second element of the product in the first row on top; the
product is then found in the intersection of the respective row
and column. Thus $D \circ B = E$. The table shows that E is the
unit element of this group of rotations since the second row is
the same as the top row. It shows that E times any element leaves
that element unchanged. The table shows that each element
has an inverse, since E occurs in every column. To find the
inverse of any element, find the element in the top row. Go
down this column until you find E. Then go to the left in this
row to find the inverse in the last column. Thus the inverse of
D is B. There is no easy way to verify the associative law from
the group table. Since the group is finite, the associative law can
be verified for all combinations of three elements.

As a final example of a group we shall consider the permutation
group on three elements. The symbol $\left(\begin{smallmatrix} 1 & 2 & 3 \\ 3 & 1 & 2 \end{smallmatrix}\right)$ is called a permu-

47

tation. It tells us that in any expression involving the numbers 1, 2, 3, the number 1 is to be replaced by 3; 2 is to be replaced by 1; and 3 is to be replaced by 2. In general a permutation on n numbers can be written as a two-line symbol. In the first line we write all the n numbers, usually in their normal order. In the second line we write under each number of the upper line that number into which it is to be changed. Two permutations are equal if they interchange the numbers in the same way. Thus

$$\begin{pmatrix} 1 & 2 & 3 \\ 3 & 1 & 2 \end{pmatrix} = \begin{pmatrix} 2 & 3 & 1 \\ 1 & 2 & 3 \end{pmatrix} = \begin{pmatrix} 3 & 2 & 1 \\ 2 & 1 & 3 \end{pmatrix}.$$

The product of two permutations is that single permutation which interchanges the numbers in the same way as the two permutations do when performed successively. Thus

$$\begin{pmatrix} 1 & 2 & 3 \\ 1 & 3 & 2 \end{pmatrix} \circ \begin{pmatrix} 1 & 3 & 2 \\ 3 & 2 & 1 \end{pmatrix} = \begin{pmatrix} 1 & 2 & 3 \\ 3 & 2 & 1 \end{pmatrix}$$

for the first permutation leaves 1 unchanged, and the second takes 1 into 3; so the product permutation must take 1 into 3. The first permutation takes 2 into 3, and the second takes 3 into 2; hence, the product permutation must take 2 into 2, i.e., must leave 2 unchanged. Finally the first permutation takes 3 into 2, and the second takes 2 into 1; so the product permutation must take 3 into 1.

We shall now show that the six permutations

$$E = \begin{pmatrix} 1 & 2 & 3 \\ 1 & 2 & 3 \end{pmatrix} \qquad A = \begin{pmatrix} 1 & 2 & 3 \\ 1 & 3 & 2 \end{pmatrix} \qquad B = \begin{pmatrix} 1 & 2 & 3 \\ 2 & 1 & 3 \end{pmatrix}$$
$$C = \begin{pmatrix} 1 & 2 & 3 \\ 2 & 3 & 1 \end{pmatrix} \qquad D = \begin{pmatrix} 1 & 2 & 3 \\ 3 & 1 & 2 \end{pmatrix} \qquad F = \begin{pmatrix} 1 & 2 & 3 \\ 3 & 2 & 1 \end{pmatrix}$$

form a group. To do so we shall construct the group table for these elements by carrying out the required multiplications.

(5)

	E	A	B	C	D	F
E	E	A	B	C	D	F
A	A	E	C	B	F	D
B	B	D	E	F	A	C
C	C	F	A	D	E	B
D	D	B	F	E	C	A
F	F	C	D	A	B	E

With the help of this table we can easily show that all of the group postulates are verified. It is of interest to note that this

48

group is not Abelian. For example $B \circ C = F$ while $C \circ B = A$.

Any one of the examples of groups which we have given shows that the group postulates are consistent. However they are not independent. For the fourth postulate is devoid of meaning if the third postulate is false since the third postulate defines an element which is needed in the fourth postulate. Despite this logical imperfection, this definition of a group is the one usually given both for historical reasons — that is how groups were first defined — and because it emphasizes some essential group properties which would have to be proved as theorems if another definition were used. To remedy the logical defects in the historical definition, we may make the following changes. We relegate the first postulate to the undefined terms. The second postulate we retain unchanged. The third and fourth we replace by the two postulates:

3′   For every A, B in G, there exists an X in G such that
$$A \circ X = B.$$

4′   For every A, B in G, there exists a Y in G such that
$$Y \circ A = B.$$

To show that the postulates 2, 3′, 4′ are equivalent to the original postulates, we must show that postulates 3 and 4 can be derived as theorems from the new postulates 3′ and 4′. The proof is as follows.

Choose any element C and let E be the solution of the equation $Y \circ C = C$. Hence $E \circ C = C$. For an arbitrary A, solve the equation $C \circ X = A$. We have
$$E \circ A = E \circ C \circ X = C \circ X = A$$
which proves 3. Since the equation $Y \circ A = E$ has a solution by 4′, we also have 4.

The following three tables establish the independence of the postulates 2, 3′ 4′. In the first table 2 is false, since

	A	B	C	D	E
A	A	B	C	D	E
B	B	A	D	E	C
C	C	E	A	B	D
D	D	C	E	A	B
E	E	D	B	C	A

	A	B
A	A	A
B	B	B

	A	B
A	A	B
B	A	B

49

$(B \circ D) \circ C \neq B \circ (D \circ C)$, while $3'$ and $4'$ are true; in the second $3'$ is false, since $A \circ X = B$ has no solution, while 2 and $4'$ are true; in the last table $4'$ is false, since $Y \circ A = B$ has no solution, while 2 and $3'$ are true.

We are now in a position to prove some simple theorems in the theory of groups. To simplify the notation, we shall omit the cumbersome multiplication symbol for group multiplication and instead indicate multiplication as in algebra by writing the letters next to each other. Thus AB will mean $A \circ B$.

Theorem 6. Every left inverse is also a right inverse.

Proof: $A^{-1} = EA^{-1}$ by postulate 3. $EA^{-1} = A^{-1}AA^{-1}$ by postulate 4. Therefore $A^{-1} = A^{-1}AA^{-1}$. Multiply this equation on the left by the inverse element of A^{-1}. Then $E = EAA^{-1} = AA^{-1}$, and we have our theorem.

Corollary. The inverse element of A^{-1} is A.

Theorem 7. The left unit E is also a right unit.

Proof: $A = EA$ by postulate 3. $EA = AA^{-1}A$ by theorem 6. $AA^{-1}A = AE$ by postulates 2 and 4. Therefore combining these results we have $A = EA = AE$.

Theorem 8. A group contains only one unit element.

Proof: By theorem 7 a unit element E is an element such that

(a) $\qquad\qquad EA = AE = A$ for all A.

If there were a second unit element E', we would have by the same theorem

(b) $\qquad\qquad E'A = AE' = A$ for all A.

In (a) set $A = E'$, and in (b) set $A = E$. We then have

$\qquad\qquad EE' = E'E = E'$ and $E'E = EE' = E$.

Therefore $E' = E$ and there is only one unit element.

Definitions. We shall call a subset H of elements of a group G a subgroup of G if all the group postulates are verified of the subset H. Thus, in the group of the rotations of a hexagon, the elements E and C form a subgroup; also the elements E, B, and D. The number of elements in a group or subgroup is called the order of the group or subgroup.

Theorem 9. The order of a subgroup H of a group G is a divisor of the order of the group.

50

$Proof:$ Let H be a subgroup of G and let the order of H be r and that of G be n. Write the r elements of the subgroup H in a row

(c) $\qquad E, A, B, \ldots, F.$

Now choose any element X of the group G and form the set

(d) $\qquad EX = X, AX, BX, \ldots, FX.$

No two elements of this set (d) are equal, for if $AX = DX$, we conclude after multiplying this equation on the right by the inverse of X, that $A = D$ which is impossible since all the elements of H are different. If X is in H, then the sets (c) and (d) consist of the same elements, namely the elements of H. If X is not in H, then (c) and (d) have no element in common. For suppose that $A = BX$, then after multiplying by the inverse element of B on the left, we should have

$$B^{-1}A = X$$

which is impossible since we have an element of H on the left-hand side of this equation and one not in H on the right. We shall call the second set (d) a $coset$ of G and designate it symbolically by HX. A coset HX therefore is either identical with the subgroup H or has no element in common with it.

Now form a second coset of G, namely HY by choosing an element Y of G not in H and not in HX. Then this second coset will have no element in common with H, and we shall prove that it has no element in common with HX. Suppose that there is a common element, say $AX = BY$. If we multiply this equation by the inverse of the element B on the left, we obtain

$$B^{-1}AX = Y$$

which means that Y belongs to the coset HX contrary to our choice of Y. So we conclude that no two cosets have an element in common. We continue forming cosets until we have exhausted all the elements of G. Therefore G may be expressed as a sum of s sets

$$G = H + HX + HY + \ldots + HK$$

of r elements each. Every element of G appears in some coset once and only once. Hence $n = rs$ and the order of the subgroup H divides the order of the group G.

THE RELATION OF MATHEMATICS TO REALITY

Since mathematics is a body of theorems derived from postulates about undefined entities, it is pertinent to ask what relation mathematics has to the real world in which we live. It will help to answer this question if we remember that no part of mathematics was developed from a set of arbitrary postulates about undefined realities. Geometry, which was the first mathematical science to assume the form of a strictly deductive science, did not begin with arbitrary postulates. At first they were considered self-evident truths about the spatial relations of the real universe. It was only the discovery of the non-Euclidean geometries which showed clearly that the postulates were not all self-evident truths, but rather statements about spatial relations which might be close approximations to the truth but not necessarily true. The postulational form was assumed by the other branches of mathematics only after they had been rather fully developed as answers to real physical problems in the real world. To determine the truth of the mathematicians' answers, we need only investigate the degree of approximation to the truth of the postulates of any branch of mathematics. If they can be interpreted as a sufficiently accurate description of the physical situation, we know at once that the whole mathematical theory will be verified in that physical situation with the same degree of accuracy with which the postulates applied. It is true, then, to say that pure mathematics does abstract from reality in the development of its various theories after the postulates have been chosen; but it is not true to say that mathematics does not reflect reality, since the postulates themselves are chosen with a real regard for reality.

What is mathematics? After having spent this chapter illustrating what mathematics is, it would be proper to end the chapter with a definition. The reason why this will not be done is the difficulty of the task. There is no single definition of mathematics which so far has been accepted and is not open to serious criticism. A volume might be written on the various definitions that have been proposed and the objections that have been raised against each of them. To give but a single illustration. In a paper at a dinner which closed a meeting of mathematicians Professor Tomlinson Fort had this to say:

"Not long ago I was chatting with a professor of philosophy when I was a bit startled by his telling me, in order to put me in my proper place in an argument, that mathematics was the science of measurement and that alone. I think he was speaking hurriedly. I also recently encountered this: 'Mathematics is the science of quantity or magnitude.' Heaven knows where this type of definition originated. . . .

"Turning to what is to us more serious, we quote Benjamin Peirce, the great Peirce, who wrote in 1870, 'Mathematics is the science which draws necessary conclusions.'"

This quotation illustrates the inability of many mathematicians to define mathematics because of their complete ignorance of philosophy. They have apparently no concept of what a definition of mathematics is supposed to be. Philosophers, on the other hand, do not understand mathematics and therefore are hardly in a better position to define what they do not know. Apparently, we shall have to await the arrival of some universal genius competent in both philosophy and mathematics before we shall have a definition of mathematics acceptable to both philosophers and mathematicians.

CHAPTER V

Modern Criticism of Euclid's Elements

We have studied Euclid's *Elements* in Chapter I, and have made efforts to approach Euclid's work in the spirit and from the point of view that prevailed in his day. In Chapter IV we have seen what modern mathematics is, and have found an entirely new approach to the subject and from a radically different point of view. For Euclid, the geometry he studied was the geometry of the universe and hence true. He accepted his fundamental propositions as self-evident truths. In the light of the discovery of non-Euclidean geometries the mathematician now knows that Euclid's view was erroneous. His geometry therefore needs a new foundation, since the old has been shown to be faulty. What is surprising is the fact that all of the Euclidean theorems can be derived from this new foundation. There is not one among them that must be rejected. It is true that Euclid's proof of many theorems is false in the light of modern rigor. The lack of consequence is due usually to the fact that he assumes tacitly what he ought to state explicitly.

Euclid begins with 23 definitions and includes in this set definitions of points, lines, and planes. These first definitions are not, properly speaking, definitions in the technical sense. Yet his geometry is to be about points, lines, and planes, and, from his point of view, it was necessary that his readers should know what his geometry was all about. They were geometric concepts of such simplicity that they could not be properly defined in terms of simpler concepts. Hence he described them in non-technical terms. The elimination of such descriptive definitions is the first change which the modern mathematician makes. He deletes the attempted definitions of point, line, and plane. These terms should be left undefined. Perhaps it would be better to say that these terms should be defined only in the postulates or fundamental, unproved propositions. It is their function to assign to the undefined terms all the properties that they are to have.

Since Euclid attempted definitions of points, lines, and planes, it is not surprising that his list of postulates does not assign to these terms all the properties that they must have to validate his geometry. He lists only five postulates, and not all of them are about points, lines, and planes. An adequate list of postulates as proposed by various mathematicians proves to be very much larger. Euclid's first proposition illustrates the case of the missing postulate. In that proposition he makes his definition of an equilateral triangle real by showing how such a triangle can be constructed, and that therefore the properties assigned to an equilateral triangle, of being a triangle and having all its sides equal, are not inconsistent. He assumes without explicit proof that a circle divides a plane into two distinct parts. This implies the continuity of lines, something he has failed to mention. Hence, speaking strictly and from the modern point of view, his proof does not conclude.

His fourth proposition is criticized for another reason. In that proposition he shows that two triangles are congruent, have all corresponding parts equal, if two sides of the one and the included angle are respectively equal to two sides and the included angle of the other. His proof is by superposition, validated by common notion four. Superposition is a natural way to verify equality, and it was used very much by all geometers who preceded Euclid, but it can hardly be classed as a proof, for a proof should show how one proposition necessarily follows from one or more others. Euclid apparently realized this as much as do modern mathematicians. He avoids proof by superposition whenever he can. He succeeds in his fifth proposition, but not in this one. Yet we need hardly wonder at this, for twenty-three centuries of mathematical thought have found no proof of this proposition in the strict sense of the term. The modern mathematician sidesteps the difficulty by making postulates of theorems which he cannot prove except by superposition.

An illustration of how Euclid's descriptive definitions of lines and planes misled him is his 16th proposition. In that proposition he attempts to prove that an external angle of any triangle (formed by one side and the extension of another) is always greater then either of the two interior and opposite angles. To see this clearly, consider for a moment some properties of points and straight lines. Two distinct points determine a straight line. Straight lines are the shortest distance between two points. Now consider a sphere instead of a plane. Any two distinct points on a sphere, if they are not at opposite ends of a diameter, determine a great circle which is the shortest distance on the sphere between the two points. (Any plane through the center of a sphere cuts its surface in a great circle.) Hence on the surface of a sphere great circles play the role of straight lines in a plane. Now there is nothing in the wording of this proposition which prohibits us from applying it to a sphere. Take a triangle on a sphere with one vertex at the pole, and the equator as one of the sides. Such a triangle is isosceles and the base angles are right angles. But so also are the exterior angles at the base. Hence Euclid's proposition is not true on a sphere. It is in general not true in any geometry in which the lines are not infinite. Hence the infinitude of the line is necessary for the validity of Euclid's proof. Yet nowhere does he state explicitly that his lines are infinite. He makes them unbounded since he tells us that they can be prolonged indefinitely. But being unbounded is not the same as being infinite. An arc of a circle is unbounded in the sense that it can be prolonged indefinitely, but it is most certainly finite since re-entrant.

It is beyond our purpose to discover all the imperfections in Euclid's remarkable work. In summary, we may say that Euclid defines too much, assumes explicitly too little, and makes tacit assumptions which invalidate any proof in which they occur. These imperfections in Euclid's work have all been removed. We now have several sets of postulates which give an adequate foundation for the geometry of Euclid. Perhaps the best known of these is that by David Hilbert. We reproduce it here.

The *undefined terms* are point, line, plane.

There are eight *postulates of connection*. (They give the relations between points, lines, planes.)

1. Two distinct points determine a straight line.
2. Two distinct points determine only one straight line.
3. There are at least two points on every line, and there are at least three points on every plane which do not lie on the same straight line.
4. Three points which do not lie on the same straight line determine a plane.
5. Three points which do not lie on the same straight line determine only one plane.
6. If two points of a line lie on a plane, then all points of the line lie on the plane.
7. If two planes have one point in common, they have at least one other point in common.
8. There exist at least four points which do not lie on the same plane.

There are four *postulates of order*.

1. If A, B, and C are points of a straight line and B is between A and C, then B is also between C and A.
2. If A and C are two points of a straight line, there exists at least one other point of the line which lies between them.
3. Of any three points of a straight line, one and only one lies between the other two.
4. Given three points A, B, and C, which are not on the same straight line, and a straight line in the plane of ABC not passing through any of the points A, B, or C, then if the line contains a point of the segment AB, it also contains a point either of the segment BC or of the segment AC (Pasch's Axiom).

There are six *postulates of congruence*.

1. If A and B are two points of a straight line a and A' is a point of the same or another straight line a', then there

57

exists on a', on a given side of A', one and only one point B' such that the segment AB is congruent to the segment $A'B'$. Every segment is congruent to itself.

2. If a segment AB is congruent to a segment $A'B'$ and also to another segment $A''B''$, then $A'B'$ is congruent to segment $A''B''$.

3. If segments AB and BC of a straight line a have only point B in common, and if segments $A'B'$ and $B'C'$ of the same or another straight line a' have only B' in common, then if AB and BC are, respectively, congruent to $A'B'$ and $B'C'$, AC is congruent to $A'C'$.

4. Given an angle (h,k) on plane a, a line $\bar{a}'$ on the same or a different plane a', a point O' on $\bar{a}'$, and on line $\bar{a}'$ a ray h' emanating from O', then on a' and emanating from O' there is one and only one ray k' such that the angle (h',k') is congruent to angle (h,k) and the interior of (h',k') is on a given side of $\bar{a}'$.

5. If the angle (h,k) is congruent to angle (h',k') and also to angle (h'',k''), then angle (h',k') is congruent to angle (h'',k'').

6. If, for triangles ABC and $A'B'C'$, AB, AC, and angle BAC are respectively congruent to $A'B'$, $A'C'$, and angle $B'A'C'$, then the angle ABC is congruent to angle $A'B'C'$, and angle ACB is congruent to angle $A'C'B'$.

The *postulate of parallels.*

Given a line a and a point A not lying on a, then there exists, in the plane determined by a and A, one and only one line which contains A but not any point of a (Playfair's Axiom).

The *postulate of continuity.*

Given any two segments AB and CD, there always exists on the line AB a sequence of points A_1, A_2, A_3, ..., A_n such that the segments AA_1, A_1A_2, A_2A_3, ..., $A_{n-1}A_n$ are congruent to CD and B lies between A and A_n (Postulate of Archimedes).

The *postulate of linear completeness.*

It is not possible to add to the system of points of a line, points such that the extended system shall form a new geometry for which all of the foregoing linear postulates are valid.

Some comments on the postulates. If you are not a mathematician, you may wonder why both postulate 1 and 2 of the first set are necessary. The reason is that postulate 1 is verified, for example, on a sphere, where any two distinct points determine a great circle, while postulate 2 is not, since if the two points are at opposite ends of a diameter, they determine infinitely many great circles.

Again in the postulates of order, the first postulate seems unnecessary, for if in passing from A to C one passes B, it seems perfectly obvious that in going from C to A one must again pass B. However this is not true on closed paths. Consider three points on a circle. If they are in the order A, B, C in passing around the circle in a clockwise direction, and if we begin at A and go to C in that direction, we must pass B, that is, B is between A and C. If now you go from C to A in the same direction, you do not pass B. Hence on closed paths if B is between A and C in one direction, it will not be between C and A in the same direction.

The postulates of congruence take care of all theorems which would have to be proved by superposition. In particular, postulate 6 of this group is essentially Euclid's proposition 4.

The last postulate, that of linear completeness, is a strange postulate, and was severely criticized by many mathematicians at the time it was first published. It is true that a set of postulates for a definite science should be complete, i.e., adequately characterize that science and distinguish it from all others. That the set of postulates of David Hilbert does that no one doubts. His last postulate, however, seems to do little more than declare that the set is complete. Now completeness is a property of a set of postulates. As such it is either present or it is not. It cannot be achieved by legislation, and this last postulate reads very much as though it were an attempt to do just that.

If you have always thought of mathematics as a science all of whose propositions are eternally true, which proves its propositions so thoroughly that all must accept the proofs as valid, the discovery of non-Euclidean geometries deprived you of part of your faith in mathematics. Since these geometries have contradictory propositions, not all of them can be true, and we do not know which are true and which are false in the universe in which we live. Now our criticisms of Euclid's proofs will have deprived you of what faith remained. You have seen that what was once considered a valid proof of a proposition is now rejected as invalid. To make matters worse, the requirements of greater rigor have been rising particularly during the past one hundred years. Nor is there any assurance that the peak of the curve of greater rigor has been reached. It may well be that what mathematicians today consider valid proofs may be rejected by their successors not many years hence, and mathematicians are the first to admit not only the possibility of such an occurrence but even its probability. Mathematics is no longer a science which has a "corner on the market" of truth, nor a science whose proofs of propositions never need revision.

CHAPTER VI

The Numbers of Mathematics

Both philosophers and mathematicians treat of numbers. The philosopher's problem is to determine the nature of the number concept. The mathematician is concerned with numbers because they and their relations may be considered to be the fundamental blocks with which the edifice of mathematics is built. When two distinct groups study the same concept from different points of view, we may expect results which are not always perfectly compatible.

PART I.   THE COUNTING NUMBERS

The first set of numbers to be devised by man was the set of *counting numbers*, or *natural integers* as they are frequently called. In the Arabic notation they are

$$1, 2, 3, \ldots$$

These numbers have been defined for us by philosophers and two definitions are classical. The first one is ascribed to Aristotle and reads *Numerus est multitudo mensurata per unum*, "number is a collection measured by a unit." It is to be noted that this definition defines a *concrete* number and not an *abstract* number. It is also worthy of note that a collection is not even a concrete number if it is not measured by a unit. Number therefore always implies the activity of an intelligent being. However, the definition, despite its distinguished authorship, is open to objection. Mathematically considered, it is imperfect among other reasons because it excludes **one** from the set of counting numbers. Both Aristotle and St. Thomas on occasion state explicitly that **one** is not a number but the measure of number.

The second philosophical definition of number, *numerus ex unitatibus constat,* "number consists of units," we owe to St. Thomas. This definition is not open to the objection raised against Aristotle's, but it seems inadequate since it would be difficult to derive from it the essential properties of the counting numbers.

A strictly mathematical definition of the counting numbers that is commonly accepted by mathematicians was formulated about 1895 by the Italian mathematician Peano. He characterizes the counting numbers by means of the five postulates:

1. There is a positive integer 1.
2. Every positive integer a has a consequent a^+. If a^+ is the consequent of a, we call a the antecedent of a^+.
3. The integer 1 has no antecedent.
4. If $a^+ = b^+$, then $a = b$.
5. Every set of positive integers which contains 1 and the consequent of every number of the set contains all the positive integers.

In this set of postulates the terms *one* and *consequent* are the undefined terms. Peano then defines addition by means of these terms.

Definition of addition: $a + 1 = a^+$. $a + b^+ = (a + b)^+$ for every a and b of the set.

Definition of multiplication: $ab = b + b + \ldots + b$ to a terms. We see from this definition that multiplication as applied to the natural integers is nothing more than repeated addition.

By means of the given postulates and the two definitions the following fundamental properties of the natural integers can be rigorously established. It will be sufficient for our purpose to accept these fundamental properties as intuitively evident.

The fundamental properties of the counting numbers

1. The set of counting numbers is closed under the operations of addition and multiplication. This means that these operations are always possible and yield a natural number.

62

2. Both addition and multiplication are associative. In symbols this means
$$a + (b + c) = (a + b) + c \qquad a(bc) = (ab)c.$$
3. Both addition and multiplication are commutative, i.e.
$$a + b = b + a \qquad ab = ba.$$
4. Multiplication is distributive with respect to addition:
$$a(b + c) = ab + ac.$$

The oldest mathematical discipline, the theory of numbers, studies the natural integers in detail. It is an interesting branch of mathematics with practically no applications. It is also one of the more difficult fields of mathematical investigation.

PART II. THE RELATIVE NUMBERS

Mathematicians have found the set of counting numbers inadequate for the task that numbers have to perform both for practical living and for the needs of the sciences. They have therefore enlarged the set of natural integers by the introduction of new numbers. The first extension of the number system owes its origin to the introduction of a new operation, namely, subtraction. We define subtraction in terms of addition by means of the following equation:
$$b + x = a.$$
In the language of every day it reads: Find a number x which when added to b gives the number a. Thus if $b = 2$ and $a = 6$, the required number x is 4. This new operation is always possible if b is less than a. It becomes impossible in the set of natural integers only if $a = b$ or if b is greater than a. To make the operation of subtraction always possible, mathematicians have enlarged the set of natural numbers. There is a way in which this may be done which puts in relief the properties of these new numbers. That method is the method of ordered number pairs.

Consider number pairs of the form (a,b) where a and b are natural integers. The order in which the numbers a and b appear in the symbol is important. (a,b) is not the same as (b,a) in most cases. To give these number pairs meaning, we shall need three definitions.

Definition of equality:
$$(a,b) = (c,d) \text{ if and only if } a + d = b + c.$$

Definition of addition:
$$(a,b) + (c,d) = (a + c, b + d).$$

Definition of multiplication:
$$(a,b)\ (c,d) = (ac + bd, ad + bc).$$

We shall now prove that the set of all number pairs obey the four fundamental laws of numbers, and are therefore numbers.

Theorem 1. *The set of all number pairs is closed under the operations of addition and multiplication.*

Proof: This theorem follows immediately from the definitions of addition and multiplication, for both the sum and the product of two number pairs is a number pair.

Theorem 2. *Addition of number pairs is commutative.*

Proof: $(a,b) + (c,d) = (a + c, b + d)$ and $(c,d) + (a,b) = (c + a, d + b)$. But $(a + c, b + d) = (c + a, d + b)$, since $a + c + d + b = b + d + c + a$.

Theorem 3. *Multiplication of number pairs is commutative.*

Proof: $(a,b)\ (c,d) = (ac + bd, ad + bc)$ and $(c,d)\ (a,b) = (ca + db, cb + da)$, and these products are equal by the definition of equality.

Theorem 4. *Addition is associative.*

Proof:
$$(a,b) + [(c,d) + (e,f)] = (a,b) + (c + e, d + f)$$
$$= (a + c + e, b + d + f).$$
And
$$[(a,b) + (c,d)] + (e,f) = (a + c, b + d) + (e,f)$$
$$= (a + c + e, b + d + f).$$

Theorem 5. *Multiplication is associative.*

Proof:
$$(a,b)\ [(c,d)\ (e,f)] = (a,b)\ (ce + df, cf + de)$$
$$= (ace + adf + bcf + bde,$$
$$acf + ade + bce + bdf).$$
And
$$[(a,b)\ (c,d)]\ (e,f) = (ac + bd, ad + bc)\ (e,f)$$
$$= (ace + bde + adf + bcf,$$
$$acf + bdf + ade + bce).$$

64

Theorem 6. *Multiplication is distributive with respect to addition.*

Proof: $(a,b) \ [(c,d) + (e,f)] = (a,b) \ (c + e, \ d + f)$
$$= (ac + bd + ae + bf,$$
$$ad + af + bc + be).$$

And $[(a,b) \ (c,d) + (a,b) \ (e,f) = (ac + bd, \ ad + bc) +$
$$(ae + bf, \ af + be)$$
$$= (ac + bd + ae + bf,$$
$$ad + bc + af + be).$$

Isomorphism. We shall say that two sets of numbers are isomorphic if there exists a one-to-one correspondence between them which preserves the operations on these numbers. Isomorphic sets of numbers differ at most in the symbols employed to represent them. Thus the two sets 1, 2, 3, ... and I, II, III, ... are isomorphic if the correspondence is 1 to I, 2 to II, etc.

Our number pairs (a,b) are of three kinds depending on the relation that exists between the numbers a and b. Either a is greater than b, or a is equal to b, or finally, a is less than b. We shall consider each of these cases in turn.

NUMBER PAIRS IN WHICH a IS GREATER THAN b

If a is greater than b, we may write $a = b + n$. Then the number pair (a,b) may be written in the form $(b + n, \ b)$.

Theorem 7. *The number pair $(b + n, \ b)$ is independent of the value of the number b.*

Proof: We must show that $(b + n, \ b) = (a + n, \ a)$ for all values of a and b. But this is obvious since $a + n + b = a + b + n$.

We now set up a one-to-one correspondence between the number pairs $(a + n, \ a)$ and the counting numbers n. We assert

Theorem 8. *The set of number pairs $(a + n, \ a)$ is isomorphic with the set of counting numbers.*

Proof: We must show that the correspondence of $(a + n, \ a) \rightarrow n$ preserves the operations of addition and multiplication. But

$$(a + n, \ a) + (b + m, \ b) = (a + b + n + m, \ a + b) \rightarrow n + m$$
$$(a + n, \ a) \cdot (b + m, \ b) = (ab + am + nb + mn + ab,$$
$$ab + bn + ab + am) = (k + mn, k) \rightarrow nm.$$

Therefore the given correspondence is an isomorphism and the number pairs $(a + n, a)$ are the natural numbers in a new notation. Something, however, has been added. These new numbers exhibit a relation between two natural numbers and state that the first is larger than the second by the amount n. To indicate this we shall call these new numbers positive integers. When their positive character is to be emphasized, we shall write

$$+1, \ +2, \ +3, \ +4, \ \ldots$$

NUMBER PAIRS IN WHICH a IS EQUAL TO b

Whenever $a = b$ in a number pair, we have a pair of the form (a,a). We assert

Theorem 9. The number pair (a, a) is independent of the value of the number a.

Proof: We must show that $(a,a) = (b,b)$ for all values of a and b. But this follows at once from the definition of equality since $a + b = a + b$.

We shall now use the symbol O to replace the number pair (a,a). This number is a definite addition to the set of integers. The following theorem gives the properties of this new number.

Theorem 10. The sum of any number and zero is that number; the product of any number and zero is zero.

Proof: $(a,b) + (c,c) = (a + c, \ b + c) = (a,b)$.

$(a,b) \cdot (c,c) = (ac + bc, \ ac + bc) = (c,c)$.

It is to be noted that zero is as much a number as any positive integer.

NUMBER PAIRS IN WHICH a IS LESS THAN b

When a is less than b, say $a + n = b$, our number pairs are of the form $(a, \ a + n)$. We assert

Theorem 11. The number pair $(a, \ a + n)$ is independent of a.

Proof: That $(a, \ a + n) = (b, \ b + n)$ for all a and b follows at once from the definition of equality.

We shall call these new numbers represented by the number

pairs $(a, a + n)$ *negative numbers* (integers) and use the more convenient symbol $-n$ to represent them. We must still investigate the properties of these new numbers.

Theorem 12. *The sum of a number and its negative is zero.*
Proof:

$$(a + n, a) + (a, a + n) = (2a + n, 2a + n) = (c,c) \to 0$$

Theorem 13. *The product of two negative numbers is a positive number.*
Proof: $(a, a + n) \cdot (b, b + m) = (2ab + am + bn + nm,$
$$2ab + am + bn) = (k + nm, k) \to nm.$$

Theorem 14. *The difference of two rational integers exists uniquely.*
Proof: We must show that the equation $b + x = a$ has a solution for all values of a and b, and has only one solution. If we substitute $a + -b$ for x in the equation, we have
$$b + a + -b = a + (b + -b) = a + 0 = a$$
so that $a + -b$ does satisfy the equation. That it is the only solution follows from the following argument. Let x' be any solution of the equation. Then
$$a + -b = (x' + b) + -b = x' + (b + -b) = x'$$
so that $a + -b$ is the only solution. This theorem proves that subtraction is always possible in the extended number system and is unique.
Definition: The set of positive and negative integers and zero is called the set of *rational integers*.

PART III. THE RATIONAL NUMBERS

We define the operation of *division*, the inverse of multiplication, by means of the equation
$$bx = a.$$
This equation asks us to find a number x of such a nature that when it is multiplied by b the product will be a. We note that this operation is not always possible in the set of rational integers. For example, there is no integer x such that $2x = 5$. In general there is never a solution of the equation unless a is a multiple of b. If then the operation of division is always to be possible, we

shall have to enlarge our number system still more. We do so again by the use of ordered number pairs.

Consider all number pairs (a,b) where a and b are any rational integers and b is never zero. We define

Equality: $(a,b) = (c,d)$ if and only if $ad = bc$.

Addition: $(a,b) + (c,d) = (ad + bc, bd)$.

Multiplication: $(a,b) \cdot (c,d) = (ac,bd)$.

Theorem 15. The set of all number pairs is closed under the operations of addition and multiplication.

Proof: The theorem follows from the definitions of addition and multiplication, for the sum and product of two number pairs is a number pair.

Theorem 16. Addition and multiplication of number pairs are commutative.

Proof:

$(a,b) + (c,d) = (ad + bc, bd) = (cb + da, db) = (c,d) + (a,b)$.

$(a,b) \cdot (c,d) = (ac, bd) = (ca, db) = (c,d) \ (a,b)$.

Theorem 17. Addition and multiplication are associative.

Proof:

$(a,b) + [(c,d) + (e,f)] = (a,b) + (cf + de, df) =$
$$(adf + bcf + bde, bdf).$$

$[(a,b) + (c,d)] + (e,f) = (ad + bc, bd) + (e,f) =$
$$(adf + bcf + bde, bdf).$$

And $(a,b) \ [(c,d) \ (e,f)] = (a,b) \ (ce, df) = (ace, bdf)$.

$[(a,b) \ (c,d)] \ (e,f) = (ac, bd) \ (e,f) = (ace, bdf)$.

Theorem 18. Multiplication is transitive with respect to addition.

Proof:

$(a,b) \ [(c,d) + (e,f)] = (a,b) \ (cf + de, df) =$
$$(acf + ade, bdf).$$

$(a,b) \ (c,d) + (a,b) \ (e,f) = (ac, bd) + (ae, bf) =$
$$(acbf + abed, bbdf)$$
$$= (acf + aed, bdf).$$

Our number pairs are of two kinds: either a is a multiple of b, say $a = bn$, or a is not a multiple of b. Let us consider each case.

Theorem 19. The number pairs (bn,b) are independent of b.
Proof: $(an, a) = (bn, b)$ for all a and b.

Theorem 20. The number pairs (an,a), under the correspondence (an,a) to n, are isomorphic with the rational integers.
Proof: $(an, a) + (bm, b) = (abn + abm, ab) \rightarrow n + m$.
$(an, a) \cdot (bm, b) = (abnm, ab) \rightarrow nm$.

Therefore the number pairs in which a is a multiple of b are new symbols for the rational integers; while the number pairs in which a is not a multiple of b represent new numbers. We shall call them *rational numbers* and use the more convenient symbol a/b to designate the number (a,b).

It is not difficult to derive all the laws of operating with these new numbers directly from their definition. For example, since $(a,b) + (c,d) = (ad + bc, bd)$, $a/b + c/d = (ad + bc)/bd$.

Theorem 21. The equation $bx = a$ always has a solution in the set of all rational numbers.
Proof: $(b,1)$ $(a,b) = (ba, b) = (a,1) \rightarrow a$. Therefore $(a,b) \rightarrow a/b$ is a solution. Conversely, let x' be any solution. Then
$$(a,b) = (bx', b) = (x',1) \rightarrow x'.$$
Therefore $(a,b) \rightarrow a/b$ is the only solution.

The set of all rational numbers is an *ordered* set. We can always determine whether two rational numbers are equal or not, and, if not, which of the two is the larger. No rational number has either an antecedent or a consequent, since between any two rational numbers there is always another. Thus, between the two rational numbers a and b is the rational number $(a + b)/2$. We designate this property of the set of rational numbers by saying that it is everywhere dense.

PART IV. IRRATIONAL NUMBERS

When a number is multiplied by itself n times, we say that the number has been raised to the nth power. Any number can be raised to any integral power in the set of all rational numbers. The inverse operation, given a number to find another number such that its nth power is the given number, is not always possible in the set of rational numbers. This statement is not obvious and requires proof.

Theorem 22. *There is no rational number whose square is 2.*

Proof: Assume that there is such a rational number a/b. Since $ka/kb = a/b$, we may assume further that a and b have no common factor. Then by our assumption

$$a^2/b^2 = 2 \quad \text{or} \quad a^2 = 2b^2.$$

This means that a^2, and hence a, must be an even number. Write $a = 2c$, and substitute this value of a in the second equation above. We have

$$4c^2 = 2b^2 \quad \text{or} \quad 2c^2 = b^2.$$

Therefore b^2 and hence b is also an even number. But this contradicts the assumption that a and b had no common factor. Hence, we have a contradiction and our original assumption that a rational number exists whose square is 2 is false. Therefore the square root of 2 is not rational.

In order that the inverse operation of raising to a power, namely extracting the root of a positive number, shall always be possible, we shall have to enlarge our number set still further so that it may include new numbers which we shall call *irrational numbers*, i.e., numbers which are not a ratio of two integers. To introduce these new numbers, we shall use a method due to the German mathematician Richard Dedekind (1831–1916). It is the method of *Dedekind cuts*.

Separate the set of all rational numbers into two classes A and B in such a way that every number of class A is smaller than any number of class B. When this has been done, the separation which we shall symbolize by (A,B) has one of the following four properties:

1) Class A contains a greatest number, while class B has no least number.
2) Class A contains no greatest number, but class B has a smallest number.
3) Class A has no greatest number and class B has no least number.
4) Class A has a greatest number and class B has a least number.

70

The property (4) was added merely to make the distribution of greatest and smallest numbers complete. Actually no cut (A,B) can have this property. For if a is the largest number in class A and b is the smallest number in class B, the number $(a+b)/2$ is a rational number which appears neither in A nor in B (it is larger than a and less than b) contrary to the rule of formation of these classes according to which all rational numbers must appear either in class A or in class B.

Properties (1) and (2) are not essentially different, for if class B has a smallest number, this can be transferred to class A, and we then have property (1). We conclude therefore that every separation of the rational numbers into two classes A and B has either property (1) or property (3). Thus if class A contains 2 and all rational numbers less than 2, while class B contains all rational numbers greater than 2, we have a separation of the rational numbers into two classes and this separation has property (1). Again if the rational numbers are separated into two classes according to the rule: In class A put all numbers whose square is less than 2; and into class B all numbers whose square is greater than 2. This will give us a separation which has property (3), for we have already shown that no rational number exists whose square is 2.

We shall now show that the Dedekind cuts (A,B) are number symbols and define a new class of numbers, the irrational numbers, whenever the separation is such as to have property (3). To do so we need the following definitions:

Equality: $(A,B) = (C,D)$ if and only if $A = C$, $B = D$.

Addition: $(A,B) + (C,D) = (A + C, B + D)$ where every number of a class such as $A + C$ consists of the sum of a number from A and a number from C. Duplicate numbers are to be dropped. A little reflection will convince the reader that $(A + C, B + D)$ is a Dedekind cut; therefore a separation of all rational numbers into two classes such that every number of the first class is less than any number of the second class.

Subtraction: $(A,B) - (C,D) = (A,B) + (-D, -C)$.

Multiplication: $(A,B)(C,D) = (AC, BD)$ where every number of a class like AC is a product of a number of A by a number of C.

71

Division: If (A,B) is a separation, then so is $(1/B, 1/A)$, where $1/A$ stands for the class of rational numbers each member of which is the reciprocal of a member of A. If zero is a member of A, it is to be omitted before forming the class $1/A$. In this case zero is added to the class $1/B$. Therefore we define division by the relation:

$$(A,B) \; / \; (C,D) = (A,B) \; (1/D, 1/C).$$

We have now defined the four fundamental operations valid in the set of rational numbers for the new symbol (A,B). That the symbol is actually a number symbol follows from the following theorems. We shall omit the proofs.

Theorem 23. The set of all possible separations (A,B) is closed under the operations of addition, subtraction, multiplication, and division.

Theorem 24. Both addition and multiplication are commutative.

Theorem 25. Both addition and multiplication are associative.

Theorem 26. Multiplication is distributative with respect to addition.

We now set up a one-to-one reciprocal correspondence between all separations (A,B) in which A has a greatest number n, and the rational number n. This correspondence is an isomorphism. Hence we have the

Theorem 27. The separation (A,B) in which A has a greatest number n is isomorphic with the set of rational numbers n.

The separations (A,B) in which A has no greatest number and B has no least number define new numbers which we call *irrational numbers*. The combined set of rational and irrational numbers is called the set of all *real numbers*.

The set of real numbers is everywhere *dense.* Between any two rational numbers, there is always an irrational number; also between any two irrational numbers there is always a rational number. Nevertheless, the set of all irrational numbers is much larger than the set of all rational numbers. The set of all real numbers is *continuous.* The proofs of some of these propositions will be given later when we come to study infinite sets.

The method of partitions cannot be used to introduce still more numbers into our set of numbers. If the real numbers are separated into two classes A and B in such a way that every number of A is less than any number of B, it can be shown that either A has a greatest real number or B has a least real number. Hence the partition defines no new numbers and would be merely a new symbol for the real numbers.

PART V.   IMAGINARY NUMBERS

The problem which led to the introduction of the irrational numbers, namely, to find the nth root of a number a, was not completely solved by the introduction of these numbers. In the set of real numbers no even root of any negative number exists. Thus there is no real number whose square is -2. More generally the equation

$$x^{2n} + a = 0$$

never has a solution for n a positive integer and any positive a. In order that this equation always have a solution, i.e., in order that all negative numbers have also even roots, we must enlarge our number system still further. We shall do so again by the use of number pairs.

Consider the set of all number pairs (a,b) where a and b are any real numbers. We make the following definitions:

Equality: $(a,b) = (c,d)$ if and only if $a = c,\ b = d$.
Addition and Subtraction: $(a,b) \pm (c,d) = (a \pm c,\ b \pm d)$.
Multiplication: $(a,b)\ (c,d) = (ac - bd,\ ab + bc)$.
Division: $(a,b) / (c,d) = \left(\dfrac{ac + bd}{c^2 + d^2},\ \dfrac{bc - ad}{c^2 + d^2} \right)$.

That the set of all pairs (a,b) under the definitions for the fundamental algebraic operations are number symbols, follows from the following theorems.

Theorem 28. The number pairs (a,b) obey the commutative law of addition and multiplication.

Theorem 29. The number pairs (a,b) obey the associative law of addition and multiplication.

73

Theorem 30. *The number pairs* (a,b) *obey the distributive law of multiplication with respect to addition and subtraction.*

The number pairs (a,b) are essentially of two kinds: either b is equal to zero or b is not equal to zero.

Theorem 31. *The number pairs* $(a,0)$ *are isomorphic with the set of all real numbers a.*

A corollary of this theorem is that the number pairs (a,b) with b not equal to zero define new numbers. These numbers are called *imaginary numbers* and the usual symbol for them is $a + bi$, where a and b are real numbers and the square of i is -1. If $a = 0$, they are called *pure imaginary* numbers. The name, of course, is unfortunate. Actually these numbers are no more "imaginary" in the dictionary meaning of that word than the positive integers. Both, as abstract numbers, exist only in the mind; both have been fashioned by the mind; for both there is an extra-mental reality which is the foundation for the numbers.

The set of all real and imaginary numbers is called the set of all *complex numbers*. The set is complete in the sense that any polynomial equation of degree n, with n a positive integer, always has n roots in the set of all complex numbers.

PART VI. HYPERCOMPLEX NUMBERS

Though the set of complex numbers is perfect and adequate for all numerical needs, the urge to generalize prompted mathematicians to look for new numbers. William Rowan Hamilton (1805–1865) discovered the first hypercomplex numbers which he called quaternions. They are numbers of the form
$$a + bi + cj + dk$$
where a, b, c, d are all real numbers and i, j, k are defined by the relations
$$i^2 = j^2 = k^2 = ijk = -1.$$

It is to be noted that these relations between i, j, k define a group of order as eight. The complete group table is the following:

74

	1	−1	i	−i	j	−j	k	−k
1	1	−1	i	−i	j	−j	k	−k
−1	−1	1	−i	i	−j	j	−k	k
i	i	−i	−1	1	k	−k	j	−j
−i	−i	i	1	−1	−k	k	−j	j
j	j	−j	−k	k	−1	1	i	−i
−j	−j	j	k	−k	1	−1	−i	i
k	k	−k	j	−j	−i	i	−1	1
−k	−k	k	−j	j	i	−i	1	−1

Though the associative and distributive laws hold for quaternions, the commutative law does not, as can easily be verified.

After Hamilton's discovery of quaternions, the notion of hypercomplex number was generalized. A hypercomplex number now is a number of the form

$$a_0 + a_1 i_1 + a_2 i_2 + \ldots + a_n i_n$$

where the a_i's are real numbers, and the i_j's are elements of a group. Hypercomplex numbers have found application in both theoretical and applied mathematics.

What we have given in very brief outline is the mathematician's view of number. It is difficult to present the modern scholastic view on the same subject since number is not one of the current interests of the philosophers. If they still accept St. Thomas' opinion, and I know of no evidence which shows that they do not, then the only numbers are the counting numbers. What mathematicians call rational numbers are not numbers but ratios in which both terms have a common measure. The same holds for the mathematicians' irrational numbers. They, too, are ratios but the two terms of the ratio have no common measure. They are ratios "non secundum numerum" (not according to number) as St. Thomas says. Complex numbers and hypercomplex numbers, of course, were unknown to St. Thomas. They were added to the collection of numbers long after the days of St. Thomas. It would be advantageous if both philosophers and mathematicians could agree on a common doctrine concerning number.

CHAPTER VII

Infinite Classes

By way of orientation we shall recall briefly some elementary philosophical definitions and divisions of the concept of infinity. An object is infinite if its perfections are not bounded by any limits (*Infinitum dicitur quod in perfectione limite caret*). An important distinction of infinity is into actual and potential. Actual infinity is predicated of an object if it has the perfection of being without limit (*infinitum actuale quod actu habet esse sine limite*); potential infinity if it is actually finite but can increase without bound (*quod actu quidem finitum est, sed augeri sine fine potest*). A line segment, for example, can be divided indefinitely. The number of divisions is always finite, but can be increased without bound. Another division of infinity is into absolute and relative infinity. An object is absolutely infinite if it is not bounded in any way (*quod sub omni respectu limite caret*); relatively infinite if it is unbounded in some respect (*quod sub aliquo respectu limite caret*). God alone is absolutely infinite; the collection of all positive integers is relatively infinite.

Since some modern scholastic philosophers insist that the concept of an infinite multitude is self-contradictory, we shall have to examine the arguments by means of which they attempt to prove their contention. If their arguments conclude, this chapter would be a waste of time and energy, and much mathematical writing of the past fifty years and more would have to be discarded. It is worthy of note that the ancient theologians and philosophers all admitted the possibility of an infinite multitude, and that not only in the intellectual order but even in the real order of existence. St. Thomas states explicitly: "It has not yet been demonstrated that God could not make actual an infinite multitude" (De Aeternitate Mundi).

Here are some of the arguments that are used to prove that the concept of an infinite multitude is self-contradictory (cf. Ontologia, Donat, pp. 141–143).

An infinite multitude is one so great that a greater one is impossible. But in an infinite multitude of men, the number of fingers is certainly greater than the number of hands, and this contradicts the definition of an infinite multitude given in the major. In this argument both the major and the minor are to be denied. The mathematical definition of an infinite set will be given later. We shall also prove that the two infinite sets mentioned in the minor are equal to each other.

If from an infinite multitude one member is subtracted, the remainder is either finite or infinite. But neither can be affirmed. For if finite, then a finite collection becomes infinite on the addition of a single unit, and this is manifestly absurd. It is not infinite, for then a part would be equal to the whole, and this also is absurd. (In this argument the second part of the minor is to be denied.) We shall show that the arithmetic of the infinite is very much different from the arithmetic of the finite. This is surprising perhaps, but might have been expected. Since infinite sets differ essentially from finite sets, we should expect that their properties would differ also.

In an infinite collection of integers, there are infinitely many multiples of two, also infinitely many multiples of three, etc. In symbols (1) $(\infty) = (2)$ $(\infty) = (3)$ $(\infty) = \ldots$ Canceling infinity we have $1 = 2 = 3 = \ldots$ which is manifestly nonsense. The fallacy in the argument is to treat an infinite class as though it were a finite number. In the proof of the minor infinity is treated as a finite number when it is deleted from both sides of the equation. Such procedure is not good mathematics. The argument is similar to the following argument which is also false. (1) $(0) = (2)$ (0). Canceling zero from both sides of the equation, we have $1 = 2$.

Among the philosophical arguments to prove that the concept

of an infinite multitude is not self-contradictory are the following (cf. *Ontologia*, Donat, pp. 143–144).

The number of things that God knows is infinite. Therefore, the concept of an infinite multitude is not self-contradictory. Certainly the number of things that God knows, particularly the possibles, is without bound; and God knows all of them, not one after the other, but simultaneously, because cognition in God excludes all succession since that is incompatible with His immutability. But by the very fact that they are known all together, they constitute an infinite collection, since of each may be predicated that it is known.

For those who maintain that the concept of an infinite multitude is inconsistent, this is a serious objection. They attempt to answer it by a twofold distinction. They say that God knows the possibles distributively and not collectively; or again that God knows them all in the simultaneity of a single act, but not in such a way that the objects known constitute a single collection. The inadequacy of such distinctions seems obvious. However, we shall let a philosopher answer their arguments. "Granted that cognition is something external to the objects known, nevertheless to each and every object, without a single exception, the predicate *known* applies. What more is required that these objects constitute an infinite collection it is impossible to see." And again: "When they say that God knows the possibles not collectively but distributively, they seem to me to give utterance to a contradiction; for since the mental reception of an object is cognition itself, and this certainly exists complete in a single instant, to say that the possibles are known simultaneously but not received simultaneously is to say that they are known and not known at the same time" (De Benedictis, Phys. 1. 3 q. 5 c. 2).

A potentially infinite multitude (which all admit) implies a multitude actually infinite. For a multitude which is potentially infinite is defined as a multitude which always remains finite, but can increase without limit, so that the mind can think of a greater and greater multitude without end. But this presupposes the possibility of a multitude actually infinite. For, since the mind does not make its object but only knows it, all parts assignable without limit must be present in the order of potency before cognition. Therefore, the concept of potential infinity implies the potential presence of infinitely many members or parts in the potentially infinite object.

Mathematicians use infinite collections. It would be rash to assert that they have permitted a self-contradictory concept to enter their domain.

A final argument. Many and greater difficulties are encountered in the study of the absolute infinitude of God than in the study of the relative infinity of sets. Yet the former difficulties are not proofs that we must abandon the doctrine of the existence of an absolutely infinite God. So likewise the difficulties and obscurities to which the concept of infinite sets gives rise are not arguments which establish the concept as inconsistent.

Before we study the mathematics of infinite classes, it will be well to examine some of the conclusions of philosophers concerning these classes which are not borne out by a mathematical study of them (cf. *Ontologia*, Donat, pp. 139–140).

An infinite multitude cannot be closed in both directions; if it were, it would be finite. Consider the set of all rational numbers which have the property that they are greater than or equal to zero but less than or equal to one. This set has a first member, namely zero, and a last member, namely one. It is closed at both ends, yet is an infinite set.

An infinite multitude cannot be a concrete number. This is true if number is defined in such a way that it must necessarily be finite. But there is no necessity for defining number in this way. There is a mathematical definition of number which does not exclude transfinite numbers. We shall have occasion to speak of them before the end of the present chapter.

An infinite multitude does not admit another infinite multitude greater than the former, so that one could be exhausted before the other. The proof: no infinite multitude can be exhausted. The reason given is true, but it does not prove that the theorem is false. As we shall see there are different hierarchies of infinity.

By way of introduction to the mathematical concept of an infinite set, we may consider infinite series. Expand the fraction $a / (1 - x)$ by actual division. We get

$$\frac{a}{1-x} = a + ax + ax^2 + \ldots + \frac{ax^n}{1-x}.$$

79

This is an identity in x and is therefore true for all values of x except $x = 1$ which would make the denominator zero. If we now assume that x lies in the interval between -1 and 1, the end points excluded, and if we allow n to become infinite, the term $ax^n / (1 - x)$ approaches zero as a limit, and for such values of x we may write

(1) $$\frac{a}{1-x} = a + ax + ax^2 + ax^3 + \ldots$$

where the three dots indicate that the series on the right goes on without end. Thus if $a = 1$ and $x = \frac{1}{10}$, we have

$$\frac{10}{9} = 1 + (\tfrac{1}{10}) + (\tfrac{1}{10})^2 + (\tfrac{1}{10})^3 + \ldots$$
$$= 1.1111 \cdots$$

Note that the equal sign presupposes that the sequence of 1's is actually infinite, not merely potentially so. For, if we take only a finite number of places in this decimal fraction, we get an approximation to the value of $\frac{10}{9}$ but not its actual value.

Another reflection suggests itself. The relation (1) is an equation, a statement of equality. The right hand side is a series containing infinitely many terms and the signs between the terms indicate that they are to be added. The left hand side is the sum of that series. This does not mean that we have actually or could actually add the terms of the series term by term; such addition is impossible. Yet we do have the exact sum of the series. If it could be added term by term, the sum would be the left hand side of (1).

In mathematics the fundamental infinite set is the set of *all* positive integers

$$1, 2, 3, 4, \ldots$$

This set has no last number. It is to be viewed not as potentially infinite, but as actually infinite. A study of the properties of this set will give us the mathematical definition of an infinite set.

If infinite sets are to be studied and compared, we must have some way of comparing two such sets. It is easy to compare finite sets. We say that two finite sets are equal if they contain the same number of objects. We determine the number of objects in each by the simple process of counting. Obviously this method of comparing sets is not applicable to infinite sets. We can never count the elements of an infinite set. *Infinitum pertransire nequit.* Therefore, if we wish to compare infinite sets, some other method must be found. A method of doing this was discovered in 1883 by George Cantor. It is the method of *reciprocal one-to-one correspondence,* a method more fundamental than the method of counting; a method which applies equally well to finite and to infinite sets. The following example will serve to illustrate the method. Suppose that we do not care to count the number of seats in a classroom nor the number of boys who are to make up the class, yet wish to know if the number of seats and the number of boys is the same. To determine this all we need do is to order the boys into the classroom and tell them to take seats. Then it is not difficult to determine by a single glance whether or not any boy or boys are standing. If not, we next determine whether there are any unoccupied seats. If then no boys are standing and there are no unoccupied seats, we know that the number of boys and the number of seats in the classroom are the same. Yet we have counted neither the seats nor the boys. What we have done is set up a correspondence between boys and seats. The inspection which revealed no boy standing and no seat unoccupied testified to the reciprocal one-to-one nature of the correspondence.

It is worth noting here that even the familiar process of counting always implies the setting up of a one-to-one correspondence which is reciprocal. What we do when we count is to set up a correspondence between the objects counted and the counting numbers. As a result, we cannot reject the method of one-to-one reciprocal correspondence as a means of comparing classes without at the same time rejecting the familiar process of counting.

To familiarize ourselves with this method, we shall use it to prove some simple theorems.

Theorem 1. There are as many negative integers as there are positive integers.

Proof: Consider the following scheme:

$$1, \quad 2, \quad 3, \quad 4, \ldots, \quad n, \ldots$$
$$-1, \quad -2, \quad -3, \quad -4, \ldots, \quad -n, \ldots$$

where the first line represents the infinite set of positive integers and the second line the infinite set of negative integers. We set up a one-to-one reciprocal correspondence between these two sets by means of the relation, n corresponds to $-n$. Obviously, to every number in the first set there corresponds one and only one number in the second set, and conversely, to every number in the second set corresponds one and only one number in the first set. We conclude therefore that there are as many negative integers as there are positive integers.

Our next illustration of one-to-one correspondence is more surprising. It is geometrical in character.

Theorem 2. There are as many points on a line segment one unit in length as on a line segment two units long.

Proof: To prove the theorem draw the two line segments AB and CD parallel to each other and draw lines through their end points. These lines will meet at some point P. To every point Q on AB corresponds just one point Q' on CD. To find this point Q', join P and Q by a straight line. This line intersects CD in Q'. Conversely, to find the point which corresponds to Q' on AB, join P and Q' by a straight line, which prolonged intersects

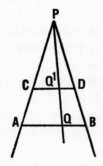

AB at Q. By means of this construction we have set up a one-to-one reciprocal correspondence between the points of the line segment AB two units long and the segment CD one unit in length. Our conclusion, therefore, must be that there are just as many points on one segment as on the other, though one is twice as long as the other. Intuitively we would be inclined to say that there must be twice as many points. Our argument shows that our intuition is not a safe guide in this instance. Many similar surprises are in store for us as we continue our study of infinite sets.

The above argument does not prove that a line segment one inch long is equal to a line segment two inches long, but merely that the number of points on both segments is the same. The argument also brings out the fact that mathematicians do not say that the points on the line generate the line. If that were the case, then in view of the above argument, all lines would be of equal length.

We shall now compare the set of all positive integers with the set of all positive even integers. The result is most surprising, for it shows that a part of an infinite set may be equal to the whole set of which it is a part.

Theorem 3. The set of all positive even integers is equal to the set of all positive even and odd integers combined.

Proof: We must again set up a one-to-one reciprocal correspondence. This can be done as indicated in the following table.

$$1, 2, 3, 4, \ldots, n, \ldots$$
$$2, 4, 6, 8, \ldots, 2n, \ldots$$

The correspondence here is of n to $2n$ and is obviously one-to-one and reciprocal.

Since such a correspondence establishes equality between sets, we see that there are just as many even integers as there are both odd and even taken together. This seems at first a patent contradiction. Certainly the even integers are only a part of the set of all integers; actually half of the set. How can half of a set be equal to the whole set? Besides what about the axiom that the whole is greater than any of its proper parts (Euclid I, C.N. 5)? Certainly we cannot abandon this axiom which is a self-evident truth. Neither, on the other hand, can we abandon the method of one-to-one reciprocal correspondence as a means of comparing sets, for the counting we do every day is nothing else than the setting up of such a correspondence between the objects counted and a part of the set of counting numbers. The solution of our difficulty lies in a re-examination of the axiom that no proper part can be equal to the whole. What is the evidence for this truth? It consists in the notions of whole and part, and in a comparison of these notions. We may ask further, whence were these notions derived? We must admit that we have acquired them by examining many wholes and their parts, and that all the wholes and parts examined were always finite wholes and finite parts. But at present the wholes and parts that we are studying are not finite but infinite. Hence, we have no valid reason to assume that what is true of finite wholes and parts must also be true of infinite wholes and parts. In fact we have seen that this is not the case. It is precisely this fact that makes our excursion into the infinite so interesting. We are entering a strange and unusual world. As an extra dividend we have also acquired a better and clearer notion of what the axiom with which we are so familiar really means.

It may be well to point out why our present theorem is not a contradiction. If we had proved, for example, that the set of even integers is a part and not a part of the set of all positive integers, we would have a contradiction and could safely abandon all further study of infinite sets. What we have shown is that there is a one-to-one reciprocal correspondence between the set of all even integers and set of all integers. Since one-to-one reciprocal correspondence in the case of finite sets establishes equality of sets, we have called the sets equal. However, another word can be used and is sometimes used. Two infinite sets between which a one-to-one reciprocal correspondence exists are said to have the same *power*. It is less shocking to say that a whole and its proper part both have the same power than to say that a part is equal to the whole. But there is another reason why the term equal is not entirely appropriate. In finite sets that are equal many one-to-one correspondences can be established, but it is impossible to set up a one-many correspondence. In infinite sets, on the other hand, even though a one-to-one correspondence exists, we can always also set up a one-many correspondence. Nevertheless, I shall use the word equal rather than power, for I have a suspicion that the word power was invented by a philosopher and not by a mathematician.

Mathematical definition of an infinite set. A set is said to be infinite if it has the property that a proper subset of the set can be put into a one-to-one reciprocal correspondence with the whole set. Less technically, a set is infinite if a part of the set is equal to the whole set.

Definition: An infinite set is said to be *denumerable* if it can be put into a one-to-one reciprocal correspondence with the set of positive rational integers.

84

Theorem 4. The set of rational numbers between 0 and 1 form a denumerable set.

Proof: Consider the set of numbers 0, 1, ½, ⅓, ⅔, ¼, ¾, ⅕, ⅖, ⅗, ⅘, ⅙, ⅚, ⅐, ... where the numbers of the set are all of the form m/n with m and n positive integers, and where m and n have no common factor other than 1, and where finally m is always less than n. This set obviously contains all rational numbers between zero and one both included. We now set up a one-to-one reciprocal correspondence between this set of numbers and the counting integers according to the following scheme:

$$0, \ 1, \ ½, \ ⅓, \ ⅔, \ ¼, \ ¾, \ ⅕, \ ⅖, \ ⅗, \ ⅘, \ ⅙, \ ...$$
$$1, \ 2, \ 3, \ 4, \ 5, \ 6, \ 7, \ 8, \ 9, \ 10, \ 11, \ 12, \ ...$$

A formula might be given embodying this one-to-one reciprocal correspondence. Since the formula would not be simple, it would not add to the intelligibility of the theorem.

Our next theorem answers an objection which might otherwise be raised when we prove later that the real numbers between zero and one, unlike the rational numbers in the same interval, do not form a denumerable set. One might argue that the real numbers by their very nature exclude a one-to-one reciprocal correspondence. The theorem will show that they do not.

Theorem 5. There is a one-to-one reciprocal correspondence between the real numbers between 0 and 1 and the set of all real numbers between 0 and 2.

Proof: Let x be real and defined by the relation $0 \angle x \angle 1$, and let y be real and defined by the relation $0 \angle y \angle 2$. Now set up a correspondence between the numbers x and y by means of the equation

$$x = y/2.$$

It is obvious that as y assumes all the values of the real numbers between 0 and 2, x varies over the set of real numbers between 0 and 1. We conclude, therefore, that there are as many real numbers between zero and one as there are between zero and two.

This theorem is the arithmetic analogue of theorem 2. In that theorem we showed that there were as many points on a line segment one unit long as on a segment two units in length.

Transfinite numbers. The counting numbers or natural integers are usually defined in such a way that the process of counting enters into the definition. Since infinite sets cannot be counted, this principle will not serve to introduce transfinite numbers. However, we have seen that counting is but a specialized way of setting up a one-to-one correspondence, and that such correspondences can be set up between infinite sets. It seems likely, therefore, that the notion of number can be generalized sufficiently to admit the introduction of transfinite numbers.

Cardinal numbers answer the question "how many?" We may define the cardinal numbers in the following manner. Consider the class of all pairs. Between any two members of this class there exists a one-to-one reciprocal correspondence. Let us define the property common to each member of the class which makes this possible as the cardinal number 2. Similarly if we consider the class of all triples. Any two members of this class have this and only this in common, that they can be put into a one-to-one reciprocal correspondence. This property common to each member of the class we define as the cardinal number three. In general, if we consider any class of sets of elements which are such that they can be put into a one-to-one reciprocal correspondence, we define the property common to every member of the class to be the cardinal number of each set in the class. If we now consider the class of all infinite sets which can be put into a one-to-one reciprocal correspondence, we may define that property of this class to be a transfinite cardinal number. The transfinite cardinal number of all infinite sets which are denumerable is designated by the first letter of the Hebrew alphabet with the subscript zero and called aleph null. It is written $\aleph_0$. We shall prove that there are other transfinite numbers.

The arithmetic of transfinite numbers. The arithmetic of transfinite numbers is radically different from the arithmetic of finite numbers, as the following two theorems prove.

Theorem 6. $\aleph_0 + \aleph_0 = \aleph_0$.

Proof: Consider the two denumerable sets
$$A = 1', \ 2', \ 3', \ 4', \ \ldots$$
$$B = 1'', \ 2'', \ 3'', \ 4'', \ \ldots$$

86

and form the set
$$C = 1', 1'', 2', 2'', 3', 3'', 4', 4'', \ldots$$
The set C obviously contains every element of both A and B, and hence is their sum. But the set C is also denumerable since we may set up the correspondence
$$2n - 1 \longleftrightarrow n', \qquad 2n \longleftrightarrow n''.$$
It is not difficult to see that to every number n of the set of all positive rational integers corresponds just one member of the set C. To the odd positive integers correspond the members of the set A; to the even positive integers correspond the members of the set B.

Theorem 7. $(\aleph_0) (\aleph_0) = \aleph_0$.

Proof: The theorem states that the product of a transfinite number by itself is that transfinite number. Recall that multiplication is nothing else than repeated addition. Thus $(a) (b) = b + b + \ldots + b$ to a terms. Hence, the theorem will be proved if we can show that the infinite set which consists of the sum of an infinite number of infinite sets, each having the cardinal number aleph null, is an infinite set whose cardinal number is also aleph null.

The following scheme proves the theorem. Each line represents an infinite set of cardinal number aleph null. There are infinitely many lines. The arrows indicate the order in which the numbers are to be taken when setting up the correspondence between the numbers in the scheme and the set of positive integers.

$$
\begin{array}{ccccccccc}
1_1 & 2_1 & 3_1 & 4_1 & 5_1 & 6_1 & 7_1 & 8_1 & 9_1 & \cdots \\
1_2 & 2_2 & 3_2 & 4_2 & 5_2 & 6_2 & 7_2 & 8_2 & 9_2 & \cdots \\
1_3 & 2_3 & 3_3 & 4_3 & 5_3 & 6_3 & 7_3 & 8_3 & 9_3 & \cdots \\
1_4 & 2_4 & 3_4 & 4_4 & 5_4 & & & & &
\end{array}
$$

From what we have seen so far of infinite sets, we might conclude that all infinite sets are equal, i.e., have the same cardinal number. This is by no means the case. There is a hierarchy among infinite sets and their corresponding transfinite numbers just as there is between finite sets and finite numbers. The set of all real numbers between zero and one, which we have already considered in theorem 5, cannot be put into a one-to-one reciprocal correspondence with the set of positive integers, as we shall now prove. Therefore, it has a cardinal number greater than aleph null. This transfinite number is called the cardinal number of the continuum and is designated by the letter C.

Theorem 8. The real numbers between zero and one form a nondenumerable set.

All real numbers whether rational or irrational can be expressed as decimal fractions. For example

$$\tfrac{1}{3} = 0.333\ldots \qquad \sqrt{2} = 1.414\ldots$$

Decimal fractions are of two kinds, terminating and nonterminating or infinite. For example $\tfrac{1}{4} = 0.25$ is a terminating decimal fraction while $\tfrac{1}{3} = 0.333\ldots$ is a nonterminating fraction.

When a number is expressed as a decimal fraction, the expression we get is not always unique. For example

$$1.000\ldots \qquad \text{and} \qquad 0.999\ldots$$

represent the same number. We can show this by multiplying the expansion of $\tfrac{1}{3}$ as a decimal fraction by 3. We obtain

$$(3)\ (\tfrac{1}{3}) = \tfrac{3}{3} = 1 = 0.999\ldots$$

To insure a unique expression for each number, we agree to replace each terminating fraction by a nonterminating fraction. This is done by diminishing the last digit in the terminating fraction by one and then following this digit by infinitely many nines. Thus 0.345 is to be replaced by 0.344999.... If we do so, then each real number will have a unique expression as a decimal fraction.

To prove that the set of real numbers between zero and one cannot be put into a one-to-one reciprocal correspondence with the set of positive integers, we assume the contrary and then show that this assumption leads to a contradiction. Suppose then that we have set up a one-to-one reciprocal correspondence between the set of real numbers between zero and one and the natural integers. This may be indicated by the following table in which the first column contains the counting numbers and the second column contains all the real numbers between zero and one expressed as decimal fractions. Each a_{ij} represents some one of the number symbols 0, 1, ..., 9.

$$1 \longleftrightarrow 0 \cdot a_{11} \, a_{12} \, a_{13} \, a_{14} \ldots a_{1n} \ldots$$
$$2 \longleftrightarrow 0 \cdot a_{21} \, a_{22} \, a_{23} \, a_{24} \ldots a_{2n} \ldots$$
$$3 \longleftrightarrow 0 \cdot a_{31} \, a_{32} \, a_{33} \, a_{34} \ldots a_{3n} \ldots$$
$$\ldots\ldots\ldots\ldots\ldots\ldots\ldots\ldots\ldots\ldots\ldots\ldots\ldots$$
$$n \longleftrightarrow 0 \cdot a_{n1} \, a_{n2} \, a_{n3} \, a_{n4} \ldots a_{nn} \ldots$$
$$\ldots\ldots\ldots\ldots\ldots\ldots\ldots\ldots\ldots\ldots\ldots\ldots\ldots$$

We shall now show that our assumption is not true, namely, that the second column contains all the real numbers between zero and one, and that therefore we have set up a one-to-one reciprocal correspondence between the positive integers and the real numbers. Consider the following number

$$N = 0 \cdot b_1 \, b_2 \, b_3 \ldots$$

where $b_1 \neq a_{11}$, $b_2 \neq a_{22}$, and in general $b_k \neq a_{kk}$. N is a nonterminating decimal fraction of a number between zero and one, yet it is not in the second column of our table which was supposed to contain all nonterminating decimal fractions. It is not in the second column because it is a number which differs in one place from every number in the set.

CHAPTER VIII

The Boole-Schroeder Algebra

Introduction. The attempt of Leibniz, the founder of the Calculus, to introduce the rigor of mathematical symbols into the other sciences may be considered the beginning of the modern subject of symbolic logic. To a very limited extent symbols were always used in logic. Symbolic logic has extended the use of symbols in logic, and, more important, has developed an algebra, the Boole-Schroeder algebra, for the correct manipulation of these symbols. Perhaps the greatest contribution of symbolic logic to the science of logic, over and above the new interest it has lent an old subject, is the fact that it eliminates many of the ambiguities so often found in words. The statements: "Nothing is greater than infinity" and "Nothing is less than any positive number" seem contradictory. Yet when these statements are written symbolically, there is no ambiguity. Thus

$$a < \infty \qquad \text{and} \qquad 0 < a,$$

where a stands for any positive number. Moreover symbols are so much more concise than words, and enable the mind to grasp a thought so much more rapidly and accurately. To illustrate this point, consider the following verbal statement of an algebraic equation: A certain number is increased by two and the sum first squared and then divided by the number diminished by one. Next the number is diminished by two and the difference first squared and then divided by the number increased by one. Finally, when this last quotient is subtracted from the first, the difference is sixteen. What is the number? Symbolically, this statement is

$$\frac{(x+2)^2}{x-1} - \frac{(x-2)^2}{x+1} = 16.$$

If you are curious about the mysterious number x which satisfies this equation, the answer is $x = 2$.

Symbolic logic is also called mathematical logic both because it is the logic used in mathematics and because logical laws are expressed in mathematical symbols and are derived from a few fundamental laws as a deductive science. It is preferred to Aristotelian logic in mathematics for reasons of convenience. Symbolic logic takes into account all of the entities with which mathematics deals, whereas Aristotelian logic does not. There is no null class, for instance, in the logic of Aristotle. To eliminate this from mathematics would be almost as inconvenient as eliminating zero from the set of numbers. Essentially, however, the two logics are the same.

To get some idea of the nature of symbolic logic, we shall develop the Boole-Schroeder Algebra as a deductive science. We shall interpret this algebra as the logic of classes to facilitate its comprehension. However the proofs of the theorems must all be managed without any appeal to the intuition which this interpretation affords. There are, of course, other interpretations of this algebra.

The Undefined Terms.
1. A class K of elements a, b, c, ...
2. An operation which we shall call multiplication by means of which two symbols may be combined and which we shall designate by writing ab.
3. Negation of a symbol which we shall indicate by writing a'.
4. Equality of symbols indicated by $a = b$.

The application we shall make of the Boole-Schroeder algebra will be to the logic of classes. Then our elements a, b, c, ... will be classes of objects. The class a, for example, may be the class of all red-covered books in the library. Now a class may be considered from two points of view, that is, we may consider a class either intentionally or extensionally. When we consider a class intentionally, we consider the property which determines whether an object belongs to the class or not. When we consider a class extensionally, we consider the objects themselves of which the class is composed. Therefore, two classes may differ intentionally but be identical extensionally. If the class a consists of all red-covered books in the library and the class b consists of all books of more than 200 pages, these two classes differ intentionally. Yet it may happen that all red-covered books in the library have more than 200 pages and that all books of more than 200 pages have red covers. Then these two classes though different intentionally would be identical extensionally since they both contain the same objects. In our application of the algebra to the logic of classes, we shall consider classes from the extensional point of view.

What meaning is to be attached to the operation of *multiplication* when applied to classes? Certainly not the meaning we attach to multiplication as applied to numbers. If a is a class all of whose members have the property A, and if b is the class all of whose members have the property B, then ab will be the class all of whose members have both the property A and the property B. Thus if a is the class of all books with red covers and b is the class of all books of more than 200 pages, then ab is the class of all red-covered books of more than 200 pages. We can make our meaning still clearer if we represent each class by a circle. The class ab will then be that portion of the plane which is common to both circles.

Negation. The negative of a class a, whose members have the property A, is the class a', the members of which do not have the property A. If the class a consists of all trout, then the class a' will consist of all objects which are not trout. Since in any discourse we do not usually speak of all possible created objects but only of a certain set of objects, which we may call the universe of discourse, the negative of any class a will not consist of all possible objects except those having property A, but only of all the objects in the universe of discourse that do not have the required property. In our example above, the universe of discourse might well be all the fish in a certain river. Then the class a' would be all the fish in the river except the trout.

Equality. Two classes will be said to be equal only if they have identically the same elements.

Definitions. We define further symbols by means of the undefined terms.

D 1. Addition: $a + b = (a'b')'$.
D 2. Inclusion: $a \subset b$ is equivalent to $ab' = aa'$.
D 3. The null class: $kk' = 0$.
D 4. The universe of discourse: $1 = 0'$.

When we translate the definition of addition in terms of the addition of classes, we have: The class of $a + b$ is the negative of the class of what is common to not–a and not–b. We can illustrate the definition by means of a diagram. The rectangle

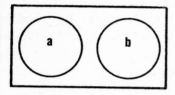 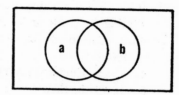

represents the universe of discourse. The two circles represent a and b respectively. Then a' is the whole rectangle except for the circle a, while b' is the whole rectangle except the circle b. Again $a'b'$, or what is common to not–a and not–b, is the whole rectangle except the circles a and b. Hence, the negative of $a'b'$ leaves the two circles a and b. So by the addition of two classes we mean all the members of a and all the members of b but without repetition. If a and b have any members in common these are counted only once in the class $a + b$.

The inclusion relation is very simple when applied to classes. It merely states that a is contained in b if there are no members of a which are not also members of b. If we translate our definition into words, it reads: a is contained in b if what is common to a and not–b is the same as what is common to a and not–a. It is to be noted that what is common to a and not–a is nothing, i.e., the null class. We define the null class in our third definition and use the symbol 0 to represent it.

The null class is one of the contributions of symbolic logic to the science of logic. Aristotelian logic does not recognize the null class, with the result that some of its conclusions differ from those of mathematical logic. But we shall return to this point when we apply our algebra to the syllogism.

In our last definition we introduce the symbol 1 to represent the universe of discourse. It is the negation of the null class.

The Postulates.

P 1. $ab = ba$. (Multiplication is commutative.)

P 2. $a(bc) = (ab)c$. (Multiplication is associative.)

P 3. If aCb, then $ab = a$.

P 4. $aa' = bb'$. (The null class is unique.)

The Axioms.

A 1. If $a = b$, then a may replace b in any expression without altering its truth or falsity and b may similarly replace a. The relation of equality $(=)$ satisfies the following postulates:

a) $a = a$. Equality is reflexive.

b) If $a = b$, then $b = a$. Equality is symmetric.

c) If $a = b$ and $b = c$, then $a = c$. Equality is transitive.

Let p, q, and r be any propositions.

A 2. From "If p, then q," we conclude "If q is false, then p is false."

A 3. From "p is equivalent to q," we conclude "p is false is equivalent to q is false."

A 4. From "If p and q, then r," we conclude "If p holds but r is false, then q is false" and "If q holds but r is false, then p is false."

It is well to note the technical difference between postulates and axioms. Postulates are always statements about the indefinables of the science. The axioms are either postulates or theorems of a presupposed science. The axioms we have listed are all, except the first, from the logic of propositions.

Note 1. That the postulates of the Boole-Schroeder Algebra are consistent follows from the interpretation of the elements as classes. The postulates in this interpretation are all obviously true about such classes.

That these postulates are independent we prove by constructing various classes of elements of which three of the postulates are

94

verified while the remaining postulate is not. These classes are given in the following tables. The first table in each set is a multiplication table, giving the products of any two elements of that set; the second table tells us what we mean by the negative of any element in the set.

: a : b : c	x : x'		: a : b : c	x : x'
a : a : a : a	a : b		a : a : c : b	a : a
b : a : b : b	b : a		b : c : b : a	b : c
c : a : c : c	c : a		c : b : a : c	c : b

Tables 1   and   1'   Tables 2   and   2'

: a : b : c	x : x'		: a : b : c	x : x'
a : a : b : c	b : b		a : a : b : c	a : a
b : b : c : a	c : a		b : b : c : a	b : c
c : c : a : b	a : c		c : c : a : b	c : c

Tables 3   and   3'   Tables 4   and   4'

Tables 1 and 1' prove the independence of postulate 1, for in that set $bc = b$, while $cb = c$. Hence, bc is not equal to cb, and so postulate 1 is false while all the other postulates are true. Tables 2 and 2' prove the independence of postulate 2; tables 3 and 3' of postulate 3; tables 4 and 4' of postulate 4.

Note 2. Axiom 1 lists the three postulates for any equivalence relation. It is of interest to show that these postulates are independent. The independence of a follows if we use the relation "is different from" for any set of numbers no two of which are alike. The independence of b follows from the relation "is a multiple of" for three numbers, the first of which is a multiple of the second, and the second a multiple of the third. The independence of c follows from the relation "differs at most by 1" for any three or more consecutive integers.

Theorem 1. If $a = b$, then $ac = bc$ and $a + c = b + c$.

By axiom 1, $ac = ac$. Replace the second a by its equal b. Then we have $ac = bc$. Similarly $a + c = a + c$. Replace the second a by its equal b to obtain $a + c = b + c$.

Theorem 2. If $a \ C \ b$, $ab' = O$ and conversely.

Use definitions 2 and 3. Thus if $a \ C \ b$, $ab' = aa' = O$. And if $ab' = O$, $ab' = aa'$, and therefore $a \ C \ b$.

Theorem 3. a C a.

$aa' = O$. Therefore by T. 2, a C a.

Theorem 4. aa = a.

If we replace b by a in P. 3, we have: If a C a, $aa = a$. But a C a by T. 3. Therefore $aa = a$.

Theorem 5. aO = O.

$aa' = O$. Hence $a(aa') = aO = (aa)a' = aa' = O$. We have used D. 3, T. 1, P. 2, and T. 4.

Theorem 6. If ab = a, then a C b.

This is the converse of P. 3. If $ab = a$, then $(ab)b' = ab' = a(bb') = aO = O$ by T. 1, P. 2, D. 3, and T. 5. Therefore $ab' = O$, and a C b by T. 2.

Theorem 7. If a = b, then a C b and b C a, and conversely.

If $a = b$, then $aa = ab = a$; and $ba = bb = b$ by T. 1 and T. 4. Therefore by T. 6, a C b and b C a. Conversely, if a C b and b C a, then $ab = a$ and $ba = b = ab = a$ by P. 3 and P. 1. Therefore $a = b$.

Theorem 8. ab C a and ab C b.

By P. 1, P. 2, and T. 4 $(ab)a = a(ab) = (aa)b = ab$. Therefore by T. 6 ab C a. Similarly $(ab)b = a(bb) = ab$. Therefore T. 6 ab C b.

Theorem 9. O C a. The null class is contained in every class.

$aO = Oa = O$ (P. 1, T. 5). Therefore O C a (T. 6).

Theorem 10. If a C O, then a = O.

If a C O, $aO = a$. But $aO = O$. Therefore $a = O$.

Theorem 11. If a C b, then ac C bc and ca C cb.

If a C b, then $ab = a$. But $(ac)(bc) = (ab)(cc) = a(cc) = ac$. Therefore ac C bc. But $ac = ca$ and $bc = cb$. Therefore ca C cb.

Theorem 12. a'' = a.

$a''a' = O$ (D. 3 and P. 1). Therefore a'' C a (T. 2). Similarly $a'''a'' = O$. Therefore a''' C a''. Therefore by T. 11, $aa''' C aa' = O$. Hence $aa''' = O$ (T. 10). Therefore a C a'' (T. 2), since a C a'' and a'' C a, $a = a''$ by T. 7.

96

Theorem 13. If $a = b'$, then $a' = b$, and conversely.

If $a = b'$, then $b = b'' = (b')' = a'$. If $a' = b$, then $a'' = (a')' = b' = a$.

Theorem 14. $a = b$ is equivalent to $a' = b'$.

By T. 13, if $a = b'$, then $a' = b$. Substitute these values of a and b in $a = b$. We get $a' = b'$. Conversely, if we substitute from T. 13 in $a' = b'$, the result is $a = b$.

De Morgan's Law: The negative of a product is the sum of the negatives of its terms; and the negative of a sum is the product of the negatives of its terms. The law bears the name of the man who first pointed it out. Our definition of a sum is an illustration of this law: $a + b = (a'b')'$. Other forms of this law follow from theorems 12, 13, and 14.

Theorem 15. $(a' + b')' = ab$.

$a' + b' = (a'' b'')' = (ab)'$. Therefore by T. 14, $(a' + b')' = (ab)'' = ab$.

Theorem 16. $(a + b)' = a'b'$.

$(a + b) = (a' b')'$. Hence $(a + b)' = (a' b')'' = a'b'$.

Theorem 17. $(ab)' = a' + b'$.

$ab = (a' + b')'$ by T. 15. Therefore by T. 14, $(ab)' = (a' + b')'' = a' + b'$.

Theorem 18. $(a + b')' = a'b$.

Theorem 19. $(a' b)' = a + b'$.

Theorem 20. $(a' + b)' = ab'$.

Theorem 21. $(ab')' = a' + b$.

The law of duality. As a consequence of De Morgan's Law, for every theorem of the algebra in terms of the relation of product, there is a corresponding law in terms of the relation of sum. This correspondence in the algebra between principles in terms of multiplication and principles in terms of addition is called the law of duality.

From the definition of the symbol 1, it follows that the symbols O and 1 are mutually negative terms. Hence we have

Theorem 22. $O = 1'$.

By applying the law of duality, we obtain a number of new theorems from our assumptions and from the theorems which we have already proved.

Theorem 23. $a + a = a$.

$a + a = (a' a')' = (a')' = a$.

Theorem 24. $a + b = b + a$.

$a + b = (a' b')' = (b' a')' = b + a$.

Theorem 25. $a + (b + c) = (a + b) + c$.

$a + (b + c) = a + (b' c')' = [a' (b' c')'']' = (a' b' c')'$. And $(a + b) + c = (a' b')' + c = [(a' b')'' c']' = (a' b' c')'$.

Theorem 26. $a + 1 = 1$.

$a + 1 = (a' 1')' = (a' O)' = O' = 1$.

Theorem 27. $a + a' = 1$.

$a + a' = (a' a'')' = (a' a)' = O' = 1$.

Theorem 28. $a' + b = 1$ *is equivalent to* a C b.

$a' + b = (a'' b')' = (ab')' = 1$. Therefore by T. 14 $(ab') = O$ and by T. 2 a C b. The converse is obtained by reversing the steps of the argument. Hence we have equivalence.

Theorem 29. *If* a C b *and* b C c, *then* a C c.

If a C b and b C c, then $ab = a$ and $bc = b$. Therefore $ac = (ab)c = a(bc) = ab = a$. Therefore by T. 6, since $ac = a$, a C c.

Theorem 30. a C b *is equivalent to* b' C a'.

This theorem enunciates what is known as the law of transposition. Its proof is as follows. If a C b, $ab' = O$ by T. 2. But $ab' = a'' b' = b' a'' = O$. Therefore again by T. 2, b' C a'. The converse is obtained by reversing the steps of the argument.

Theorem 31. a C b' *is equivalent to* b C a'.

Theorem 32. a' C b *is equivalent to* b' C a.

Theorem 33. $a + b = b$ *is equivalent to* a C b.

If $a + b = b$, then $a + b = (a' b')' = b$ by D. 1, and $a' b' =$

$b' a' = b'$ by P. 1 and T. 14. Therefore $b' C a'$ which is equivalent to $a C b$ by T. 30. Conversely, if $a C b$, $b' C a'$ and $b' a' = b'$. Hence $(b' a')' = b'' = b = b + a = a + b$.

Theorem 34. $a C a + b$ **and** $b C a + b$.

By T. 8 $a' b' C a'$ and $a' b' C b'$. Therefore by T. 30 $a C (a' b')' = a + b$ and $b C (a' b')' = a + b$.

Theorem 35. $a C 1$.

By T. 9 $O C a'$. Therefore by T. 30 $a C O' = 1$.

It is worthy of note that the two laws $a C 1$ and $O C a$ are equivalent. The admission of one requires the admission of the other. Scholastic philosophers easily admit the former, but do not admit the latter on the ground that O is a meaningless symbol when applied to classes.

Theorem 36. $a1 = a$.

Since $a C 1$, $a1 = a$ by P. 3.

Theorem 37. $a + O = a$.

By T. 36 $a' 1 = a'$. Therefore by T. 13 and D. 1, $a = (a' 1)' = a + O$.

Theorem 38. $1 C a$ **is equivalent to** $a = 1$.

By P. 3 $1 C a$ means $1a = 1$. By T. 36 $1a = a$. Therefore $a = 1$. By reversing the steps of the argument we obtain the converse.

Theorem 39. If $a C b$ **and** $c C d$, **then** $ac C bd$.

If $a C b$ and $c C d$, then $ab = a$ and $cd = c$. Therefore $(ac) (bd) = (ab) (cd) = ac$. Hence $ac C bd$ by T. 6.

Theorem 40. If $a C b$ **and** $c C d$, **then** $a + c C b + d$.

If $a C b$ and $c C d$, then by T. 30 $b' C a'$ and $d' C c'$. Therefore by T. 39 and T. 30 $b'd' C a' c'$ and again by T. 30 $(a' c')'$ $C (b' d')'$. Therefore by D. 1, $a + c C b + d$.

Theorem 41. If $a C c$ **and** $b C c$, **then** $a + b C c$.

Set $d = c$ in T. 40 and remember that $aa = a$ and $a + a = a$.

Theorem 42. If $a C b$ **and** $a C c$, **then** $a C bc$.

The proof follows if you set $c = a$ and $d = c$ in T. 39.

Theorem 43. If $a \subset b$, then $a + c \subset b + c$.

By T. 3 $c \subset c$. From $a \subset b$ and $c \subset c$ by T. 40 $a + c \subset b + c$.

Theorem 44. $ab \subset a + b$.

By T. 8, $ab \subset a$ and by T. 34 $a \subset a + b$. Therefore by T. 29 $ab \subset a + b$.

Theorem 45. $a(b + c) = ab + ac$.

1. We first prove that $(ab + ac) \subset a(b + c)$. Since by T. 3 $a \subset a$ and by T. 34 $b \subset b + c$, we have by T. 34 $ab \subset a(b + c)$. Similarly $ac \subset a(b + c)$. Therefore by T. 41 $(ab + ac) \subset a(b + c)$.

2. We now prove that $a(b + c) \subset (ab + ac)$. Since $a(ab)'b = (ab)(ab)' = O$, $a(ab)' \subset b'$ by T. 2. Similarly $a(ac)' \subset c'$. Therefore $a(ab)'(ac)' \subset b'c'$ by T. 39. Therefore by T. 2, $a(ab)'(ac)'(b'c')' = O = a(b'c')'[(ab)'(ac)']''$. Therefore $a(b'c')' \subset [(ab)'(ac)']'$. Therefore by D. 1, $a(b + c) \subset (ab + ac)$. Now combine 1 and 2 by means of T. 7; we obtain $a(b + c) = ab + ac$.

Theorem 46. $(a + b)(c + d) = ac + bc + ad + bd$.

To prove the theorem apply T. 45 twice.

The following theorem states the *Law of Absorption* which is constantly used to simplify expressions.

Theorem 47. If a term in a sum of products appears by itself, then all other products containing this term may be dropped. In symbols: $a + ab = a$.

By T. 34 $a \subset a + ab$. We next prove that $a + ab \subset a$. Since $a \subset a$ and by T. 8, $ab \subset a$, T. 40 gives $a + ab \subset a$. Therefore by T. 7, $a + ab = a$.

The Law of Expansion. If a given expression does not contain a certain term, we can always find an equivalent expression which does. The law which enables us to do so is called the law of expansion and is formulated in the following theorems.

Theorem 48. $a = a(b + b') = ab + ab'$.

By T. 36, $a = a1$ and by T. 27, $1 = b + b'$.

When we write $1 = b + b'$, we have expanded the universe in terms of one element. We can expand the universe in terms of

100

as many elements as we please since $1 = (1) (1) \ldots$. The expansion of the universe in terms of two elements is
$$1 = (a + a') (b + b') = ab + a'b + ab' + a'b'.$$
The total number of terms in the expansion of the universe in terms of n elements is 2 raised to the power n.

We shall call an expression *fully expanded* when every element which appears in the expression, or the negative of that element, appears in every term. Thus $ab' + a'b + a'b'$ is fully expanded, for a or a' and b or b' appear in every term. On the other hand, $a + a'b$ is not fully expanded since neither b nor b' appear in the first term. Here the fully expanded expression will be found by expanding the first term so as to introduce b. Thus
$$a + a'b = a(b + b') + a'b = ab + ab' + a'b.$$
To find the *negative* of a complicated expression, we first give it the fully expanded form and then find the negative by the simple rule: the negative of any fully expanded expression is the remainder of the expansion of 1. For example, since
$$1 = ab + ab' + a'b + a'b'$$
the negative of $ab' + a'b$ is $ab + a'b'$.

Theorem 49. $a + b = a + a'b$.
$a + b = a + b(a + a') = a + ba + ba' = a + ba'$.

Theorem 50. If $a + b = x$ and $a = O$, then $b = x$.
$a + b = O + b = b = x$.

Theorem 51. $a + b = O$ *is equivalent to the pair* $a = O$, $b = O$.

If $a + b = O$, then $a'b' = 1$. Hence $a = a1 = a(a'b') = (aa')b' = Ob' = O$. And $b = b1 = (a'b')b = a'(bb') = a'O = O$. Finally, if $a = O$ and $b = O$, $a + b = O + O = O$.

If we apply the law of duality to the last two theorems, we obtain

Theorem 52. If $ab = x$ and $a = 1$, then $b = x$.

Theorem 53. $ab = 1$ *is equivalent to the pair* $a = 1$, $b = 1$.

The following theorems concern equivalent equations of various forms. The first of these enables us to change an equation into one in which one member is zero. It is equivalent to the transposition of terms in ordinary algebra.

Theorem 54. $a = b$ *is equivalent to* $ab' + a'b = O$ *and to* $ab + a'b' = 1$.

By T. 7, $a = b$ is equivalent to $a \, C \, b$ and $b \, C \, a$. But by T. 2, $a \, C \, b$ means $ab' = O$ and $b \, C \, a$ means $ba' = O$. Therefore by T. 51, $ab' + a'b = O$. Apply T. 14 to this equation. We have $(ab' + a'b)' = 1 = ab + a'b$ (which is the negative of $ab' + a'b$.)

Theorem 55. $a = O$ *is equivalent to* $t = at' + a't$.

This theorem is known as *Poretsky's Law of Form*. Obviously, if $a = O$, $t = at' + a't$ since $at' = O$ and $a't = t$. To obtain the converse, apply T. 54 to the equation $t = at' + a't$, i.e., multiply each side of the equation by the negative of the other, add the products, and equate them to zero. We have

$$O = t(at'+a't)' + t'(at' + a't) = t[(at')'(a't)'] + at' + a'O$$
$$= t[(a' + t)(a + t')] + at' = t(at + a't') + at' = at + at'$$
$$= a(t + t') = a.$$

Theorem 56. $a = b$ *is equivalent to* $t = (ab' + a'b)t' + (ab + a'b')t$.

If we substitute $a = b$ in the given relation and simplify, we get the identity $t = t$. To obtain the converse, apply T. 54 to the given relation in t as in the preceding theorem.

Functions. Any expression involving one or more variable quantities $x, y, \ldots$ and the operations of addition $(+)$ and multiplication but not the relations of equality $(=)$ or "is contained in" (C) will be called a function. The *normal form* of a function of one variable x is $ax + bx'$. Any function in one variable can be given this normal form. Suppose, for example, that we wish to treat $ax + b + x'c$ as a function of x and reduce it to normal form. Since this function contains one term free of x or x', we expand that term with respect to x and collect the coefficients of x and x'. Thus $ax + b + x'c = ax + b(x + x') + x'c = ax + bx + bx' + cx' = (a + b)x + (b + c)x'$.

Theorem 57. $(ax + bx') + (cx + dx') = (a + c)x + (b + d)x'$. This theorem follows immediately from T. 45.

Theorem 58. $(ax + bx')(cx + dx') = acx + bdx'$.

102

Theorem 59. $(ax + bx')' = a'x + b'x'$.

$(ax + bx')' = (ax)'(bx')' = (a' + x')(b' + x) = a'b' + a'x + b'x' + O = a'b'(x + x') + a'x + b'x' = (a'b' + a')x + (a'b' + b')x' = a'x + b'x'$, since by T. 47 $a'b' + a' = a'$ and $a'b' + b' = b'$.

Theorem 60. If $f(x) = ax + bx'$, then $f(1) = a$ and $f(O) = b$. Therefore $f(x) = f(1)x = f(O)x'$.

Theorem 61. $f(1) = f(a + b) = f(a' + b')$.

Theorem 62. $f(O) = f(ab) = f(a'b')$.

Theorem 63. $f(a) = a + b = f(b') = f(ab') = f(a + b') = f(1) + f(O) = f(x) + f(x')$.

Theorem 64. $f(b) = ab = f(a') = f(a'b) = f(a' + b) = [f(1)][f(O)] = [f(x)][f(x')]$.

The normal form of a function of two variables x and y will be $axy + bx'y + cxy' + dx'y'$. In general, the normal form of a function in any number of variables is found by giving a coefficient to each term in the expansion of 1 in those variables.

We now consider some important laws concerning the limits of functions.

Theorem 65. The lower limit of a function is the product of the coefficients; the upper limit is the sum of the coefficients. In symbols: $ab\,C\,ax + bx'\,C\,a + b$.

$ab(ax + bx') = abx + abx' = ab(x + x') = ab$. Therefore by T. 6, $ab\,C\,ax + bx'$. Again $(ax + bx')(a + b)' = (ax + bx')(a'b') = O$. Therefore by D. 2, $ax + bx'\,C\,a + b$.

Theorem 66. If $ax + bx' = O$, then $ab = O$.
Since $ab\,C\,ax + bx' = O$, $ab = O$ by T. 10.

Theorem 67. If $ax + bx' = 1$, then $a + b = 1$.
Since $1 = ax + bx'\,C\,a + b$, $a + b = 1$ by T. 38.

Note. The last two theorems serve as the formulae for the elimination of any element x from an equation. Since every equation can be given the form in which one member is O, theorem 66 can always be applied and is the principle most frequently used. Logically, this principle is very important since in

103

every syllogism we must eliminate the middle term to arrive at the conclusion.

Another logically important operation of the algebra is the solution of equations. In general, an equation determines the value of the variable only between limits.

Theorem 68. $ax + bx' = O$ *is equivalent to* $b \, C \, x \, C \, a'$.

By T. 51 $ax + bx' = O$ is equivalent to the pair $ax = O$, $bx' = O$. But by T. 2 $ax = O$ is equivalent to $x \, C \, a'$, and $bx' = O$ is equivalent to $b \, C \, x$. Obviously, this solution will be unique if and only if the two limits coincide.

Theorem 69. $a' \, x + ax' = O$ *is equivalent to* $x = a$.

By T. 68 $a \, C \, x \, C \, a$. Therefore by T. 7, $x = a$.

Theorem 70. $ax + bx' = 1$ *is equivalent to* $b' \, C \, x \, C \, a$.

By T. 14, if $ax + bx' = 1$, then $(ax + bx')' = O$. By T. 59, $(ax + bx')' = a' \, x + b' \, x' = O$. Therefore by T. 68, $b' \, C \, x \, C \, a$.

Theorem 71. $ax + bx' = cx + dx'$ *is equivalent to* $(bd' + b' \, d)$ $C \, (ac + a' \, c')$.

By T. 54, $ax + bx' = cx + dx'$ is equivalent to $(ax + bx')$ $(cx + dx')' + (ax + bx')' (cx + dx') = O$. But by T. 59 $(cx + dx')' = c' \, x + d' \, x'$ and $(ax + bx')' = a' \, x + b' \, x'$. By T. 58, $(ax + bx') (c' \, x + d' \, x') + (a' \, x + b' \, x') (cx + dx') = ac' \, x + bd' \, x' + a' \, cx + b' \, dx' = (ac' + a' \, c)x + (bd' + b' \, d)x'$. By T. 68, $(ac' + a' \, c)x + (bd' + b' \, d)x' = O$ is equivalent to $bd' + b' \, d \, C \, x \, C \, ac' + (a' \, c)' = ac + a' \, c'$ by T. 59.

Note. Our solutions of equations have been in the form of inequalities. The solutions may also be put in the form of equations as in ordinary algebra. From the logical point of view this is not important. We shall, however, solve the equation of theorem 68 to obtain a solution in the form of an equation.

Theorem 72. If $ax + bx' = O$, then for some undetermined value of u, $x = bu' + a' \, u = b + a' \, u$.

Substituting $x = bu' + a' \, u$ in $ax + bx' = O$, we have $a(bu' + a' \, u) + b(bu' + a' \, u)' = a(bu' + a' \, u) + (b' \, u' + au)b = abu' + abu = ab(u' + u) = ab$. But by T. 66, if $ax + bx' = O$, then $ab = O$. Therefore if $ab = O$ as the given equation requires, then

104

the equation is satisfied by $x = bu' + a'u$. Moreover, if $ab = O$, then $abu = O$ and therefore $bu' + a'u = bu' + a'u + abu = bu' + a'(b + b')u + abu = bu' + a'bu + a'b'u + abu = bu' + (a + a')bu + a'b'u = b(u' + u) + a'b'u = b + b'(ua') =$ (by T. 49) $b + ua'$. Therefore, if $ab = O$, then $bu' + ua' = b + a'u$.

Note. The limiting values of u are O and 1. If $u = O$, then $bu' + a'u = b$, and if $u = 1$, $bu' = a'u = a'$. Therefore this form of the solution expresses the same fact as $b \, C \, x \, C \, a'$

In applying the algebra to the processes of reasoning, we shall need *inequations* in addition to equations. We shall need the following theorems which follow at once from the theorems listed in parentheses which we have already proved, and one or another of our axioms.

Theorem 73. If $ac \neq bc$, then $a \neq b$ (T. 1).

Theorem 74. of $a + c \neq b + c$, then $a \neq b$ (T. 1).

Theorem 75. The *following are all equivalent*: $ab \neq a$, $ab' \neq O$, $a' + b \neq 1$, $a + b \neq b$, and each of these is equivalent to "It is false that $a \, C \, b$." (P. 3, T. 2, T. 28, T. 33).

Theorem 76. If $a + b = x$ and $b \neq x$, then $a \neq O$ (T. 50).

Theorem 77. If $a = O$ and $b \neq x$, then $a + b \neq x$ (T. 50).

Theorem 78. If $a + b \neq O$ and $a = O$, then $b \neq O$ (T. 51).

Theorem 79. If $a \neq O$, then $a + b \neq O$ (T. 51).

Theorem 80. If $ab \neq O$, then $a \neq O$ (T. 5).

Theorem 81. If $a + b \neq 1$, then $a \neq 1$ (T. 26).

Theorem 82. If $ab \neq x$, and $a = x$, then $b \neq x$ (T. 4).

Theorem 83. If $a \neq O$ and $a \, C \, b$, then $b \neq O$.

By P. 3, if $a \, C \, b$, then $ab = a$. Therefore, if $a \neq O$ and $a \, C \, b$, then $ab \neq O$. But by T. 81, if $ab \neq O$, then $b \neq O$.

Theorem 84. $a \neq b$ is equivalent to $ab' + a'b \neq O$ (T. 54).

Theorem 85. $a \neq O$ is equivalent to $t \neq at' + a't$ (T. 55).

105

Theorem 86. $a \neq b$ *is equivalent to* $t \neq (ab' + a'b)t' + (ab + a'b')t$ (T. 56).

Theorem 87. If $ax + bx' \neq O$, **then** $a + b \neq O$.

By T. 24 $(ax + bx')$ $C(a + b)$. Hence, the theorem follows from T. 83.

Most of the theorems of the algebra have been proved only for two letters. They are true for any number of letters as can easily be shown by induction. But the reader is doubtless weary of proofs by this time, and will be grateful to the author for omitting further proofs and proceeding to applications of the algebra. These will be found in the following chapter.

CHAPTER IX

Applications of the Boole-Schroeder Algebra

The reader may have found the preceding chapter rather difficult unless he has been blessed with a talent for mathematics. It is even highly probable that he has been satisfied with working out the proofs of very few of the theorems. In the present chapter we shall show how the theorems can be used, and in this way the chapter may motivate a re-reading of its predecessor. We hope to show that symbolic logic has advantages which it does not share with Aristotelian logic. Our application of the algebra will be confined to a study of the syllogism and the square of opposition.

Consider the syllogism: All goats are animals. All animals are mortal. Therefore all goats are mortal. If we symbolize goats by g, animals by a, and mortality by m, our syllogism in symbolic form will become:

$$\text{All } g \text{ is } a\text{: } ga = O.$$
$$\text{All } a \text{ is } m\text{: } am' = O.$$
$$\text{Therefore all } g \text{ is } m\text{: } gm' = O.$$

How can we obtain this conclusion from our algebra? If we add the equations of the premises, which we may do by T. 1 and T. 23, we obtain $ga' + am' = O$. We next apply T. 66 which states that if $ax + bx' = O$, then $ab = O$. Here we must set $x = a$ since it is the only element which appears positive in one term and negative in the other. We therefore obtain $gm' = O$ which is the required solution.

Next consider a syllogism in which one premise is particular. For example: All sins are evil. Some sins are lies. Therefore some evils are lies. Symbolize sins by s, evils by e, and lies by L. Our syllogism then becomes:

$$\text{All } s \text{ is } e: se' = O.$$
$$\text{Some } s \text{ is } L: sL \neq O.$$
$$\text{Therefore some } e \text{ is } L: eL \neq O.$$

We obtain this conclusion from our algebra in the following way. Expand both premises so that they contain all the elements.

$$se' = se'(L + L') = se'L + se'L' = O.$$
$$sL = sL(e + e') = sLe + sLe' \neq O.$$

From the first equation, by means of T. 51, we conclude that $se'L = O$. Next we apply T. 78 to the second relation to obtain $seL \neq O$. Finally, we apply T. 80 to $seL \neq O$ to obtain $eL \neq O$, which is our syllogistic conclusion.

When we apply the algebra to a false syllogism, one of two situations will arise: if a true conclusion is possible from the premises, the algebra will give the correct conclusion; if no conclusion is possible, the algebra will exhibit equations or an equation and an inequation which are incompatible and have no solution. For example, consider the syllogism: All books are interesting. All plays are interesting. Therefore all plays are books. Set b = books, i = interesting, p = plays. We then have:

$$\text{All } b \text{ is } i: bi' = O.$$
$$\text{All } p \text{ is } i: pi' = O.$$
$$\text{Therefore all } p \text{ is } b: pb' = O.$$

If we add the first two equations, we obtain the equation $bi' + pi' = O$. This equation cannot be solved by T. 66 or any other theorem since it contains no element which is positive in one term and negative in the other. Therefore, there is no legitimate conclusion from the given premises. An examination of these premises show that they commit the fallacy of the undistributed middle term.

The same holds if the incorrect syllogism contains a particular premise. Consider the syllogism: All men are animals. Some animals are dogs. Therefore some men are dogs. Let m = man, animal = a, and dog = d. We then have

All m is a: $ma' = O$.

Some a is d: $ad \neq O$.

Therefore some m is d: $md \neq O$.

If we expand the premises so that they contain all terms, we have

$$ma' = ma'(d + d') = ma'd + ma'd' = O.$$
$$ad = ad(m' + m') = adm + adm' \neq O.$$

Since this equation and inequation have no term in common, they cannot be combined and hence no solution is possible. The syllogism is not a valid syllogism.

Another test for the validity of any syllogism is what is sometimes called the inconsistent triad. If we take any valid syllogism and replace the conclusion by its contradictory, we get a set of three propositions any two of which establish the truth of the contradictory of the third. For example the syllogism: All men are animals. All animals are mortal. Therefore all men are mortal. If we replace the conclusion by its contradictory, some men are not mortal, we obtain the inconsistent triad:

All men are animals. $ma' = O$.

All animals are mortal. $ad' = O$.

Some men are not mortal. $md' \neq O$.

From this triad we obtain the following three valid syllogisms by combining two of the propositions with the contradictory of the third.

1. All men are animals.
   All animals are mortal.
   Hence all men are mortal.
2. All men are animals.
   Some men are not mortal.
   Hence some animals are not mortal.
3. All animals are mortal.
   Some men are not mortal.
   Hence some men are not animals.

The principle on which the inconsistent triad is based was recognized even in the days of Aristotle. It is this: If two premises give a conclusion and if one of the premises is true but the conclusion false, then the other premise must be false.

As a further illustration let us take a syllogism with a particular premise: No man is an angel. Some angels are devils. Therefore some devils are not men. The inconsistent triad is:

No man is an angel. $ma = O$.
Some angels are devils. $ad \neq O$.
All devils are men. $dm' = O$.

The effectiveness of the inconsistent triad as a check on the validity of a syllogism is the fact that all inconsistent triads have the same pattern when expressed in symbols. There are always: (1) Two equations and one inequation. (2) The two equations always have one element in common which is positive in one and negative in the other. (3) The inequation will always combine the other two elements appearing in the equations with whatever signs they there have.

Let us apply this test to the following syllogism. No Jesuit is a Franciscan. Some Franciscans are Capuchins. Hence some Jesuits are not Capuchins. If $j = $ Jesuits, $f = $ Franciscan, and $c = $ Capuchin, our syllogism in symbolic form reads:

No j is f: $jf = O$.
Some f is c: $fc \neq O$.
Hence some j is not c: $jc' \neq O$.

The corresponding inconsistent triad has the form: $jf = O$, $fc \neq O$, $jc' = O$. Here we have two equations and one inequation. However, the letter j which is common to the two equations does not appear negative in one equation and positive in the other. Hence we conclude that the syllogism is false. We can get the correct conclusion by means of our algebra. Expand each of the premises so as to contain all terms:

$$jf = jf(c + c') = jfc + jfc' = O.$$
$$fc = fc(j + j') = fcj + fcj' \neq O.$$

By T. 51 we conclude that $jcf = O$. If $jcf = O$, then by T. 78 $j'cf \neq O$. Finally by T. 80 and the fact that $j'cf \neq O$, we conclude that $j'c \neq O$. This is the correct conclusion, namely, "Some Capuchins are not Jesuits."

Let us next apply our test to a syllogism in the third figure with two universal premises and a particular conclusion. For example: All absentees receive a grade of zero. No absentees are

110

failed. Therefore some who receive a grade of zero do not fail. In symbols we have

$$\text{All } a \text{ is } z: az' = O.$$
$$\text{No } a \text{ is } f: af = O.$$
$$\text{Therefore some } z \text{ is not } f: zf' \neq O.$$

The inconsistent triad here has the following pattern: $az' = O$, $af = O$, $zf' = O$. Here we have three equations instead of two equations and an inequation, and we conclude that the syllogism is not valid though it is a syllogism sanctioned by Aristotle.

Since the test of the inconsistent triad for the validity of a syllogism may seem arbitrary, it will be well to prove more in detail that a particular conclusion may never be drawn from a universal statement or from any number of universal statements. The syllogisms of the third and fourth figures in some moods commit this fallacy — fallacy from the point of view of symbolic logic — for in both figures the premises may be universal and the conclusion particular.

For proof we appeal to our algebra. We have seen that if $a = O$, then $a\,C\,b$ and $a\,C\,b'$ by T. 9. Moreover by T. 5, if $a = O$, then $ab = O$ and $ab' = O$. Therefore, if $a = O$, both $ab \neq O$ and $ab' \neq O$ must be false. Here $ab = O$ is the symbol for the universal negative proposition: No a is b; $ab' = O$ symbolizes the universal affirmative proposition: All a is b. The corresponding particular propositions are: Some a is b: $ab \neq O$; and some a is not b: $ab' \neq O$. Therefore, if $a = O$, the universal propositions "All a is x, No a is y" are always true no matter what x and y may be, while the corresponding particular propositions "Some a is x and Some a is not y" are always false.

The reason for the disagreement between Aristotelian and symbolic logic is the fact that Aristotelian logic does not recognize the null class, whereas symbolic logic does. A further reason, or better the same reason put in another way, is the interpretation of the word all. For Aristotle all means two things: (1) There are no exceptions; (2) There is at least one. In symbolic logic all means only "there are no exceptions."

If we should ask the further question: Which logic is the correct logic, Aristotelian or symbolic? The answer would be

111

that they are both consistent. In any situation where the null class cannot occur, Aristotelian logic is perfectly adequate. Wherever the null class does occur, for example in mathematics, symbolic logic must be used.

As a final illustration of the differences between the two kinds of logic, we shall consider the square of opposition. In Aristotelian logic the square has the following properties. The

All a is b: $ab' = O$.   No a is b: $ab = O$.

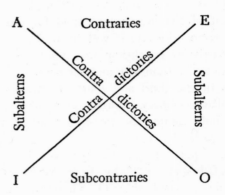

Some a is b: $ab \neq O$.   Some a is not b: $ab' \neq O$.

contraries A and E may both be false but cannot both be true. Subcontraries I and O may both be true but cannot both be false. Subalterns A and I or E and O are either both true or both false. Contradictories cannot both be true or both be false. In symbolic logic, because of the presence of the null class, none of these properties can be admitted except the last one: Contradictories cannot both be true or both be false. In symbolic logic we can always argue to the truth or falsity of one of a pair of contradictories from the truth or falsity of the other. It is a curious fact that the only proposition about the square of opposition which is universally true in symbolic logic is precisely the one which is not always true in Aristotelian logic. According to Aristotle, one member of a pair of contradictories may be false while the other is meaningless.

112

Immediate inference from a universal to a particular which is legitimate in Aristotelian logic becomes a mediate inference in symbolic logic by making the assumption of existence explicit. Thus suppose that we are given: All a is b: $ab' = O$, and a exists: $a \neq O$. We then may infer by the algebra:

$$a = a(b + b') = ab + ab' \neq O.$$

But $ab' = O$. Therefore $ab \neq O$, i.e., some a is b.

Similarly for the syllogisms of the third and fourth figures. If we supply the assumption of existence, they cease to be syllogisms. Thus suppose that we have given: No b is c: $bc = O$. All b is a: $ba' = O$. And b exists: $b \neq O$. We may then proceed as follows:

$b = b(a + a') = ab + a'b \neq O.$

But $a'b = O$. Therefore (T. 78) $ab \neq O$.

Again $ab = ab(c + c') = abc + abc' \neq O$.

And $bc = bc(a + a') = abc + a'bc = O$.

Therefore $abc = O$ and (T. 78) $abc' \neq O$.

Finally since $abc' \neq O$, $ac' \neq O$, or some a is not c.

The above argument may seem complex, but it or a similar argument is necessary if we are to draw a valid particular conclusion from universal premises wherever the null class is not automatically excluded.

But it is high time that I return whence I came to my ivory tower.

113

Appendix

EUCLID'S ELEMENTS, BOOK I

(Proofs have been omitted)

DEFINITIONS

1. A *point* is that which has no part.
2. A *line* is breadthless length.
3. The extremities of a line are points.
4. A *straight line* is a line which lies evenly with the points on itself.
5. A *surface* is that which has length and breadth only.
6. The extremities of a surface are lines.
7. A *plane surface* is a surface which lies evenly with the straight lines on itself.
8. A *plane angle* is the inclination to one another of two lines in a plane which meet one another and do not lie in a straight line.
9. And when the lines containing the angle are straight, the angle is called *rectilineal*.
10. When a straight line set up on a straight line makes the adjacent angles equal to one another, each of the equal angles is *right*, and the straight line standing on the other is called a *perpendicular* to that on which it stands.
11. An *obtuse angle* is an angle greater than a right angle.
12. An *acute angle* is an angle less than a right angle.
13. A *boundary* is that which is an extremity of anything.
14. A *figure* is that which is contained by any boundary or boundaries.
15. A *circle* is a plane figure contained by one line such that all the straight lines falling upon it from one point among those lying within the figure are equal to one another;

16. And the point is called the *center* of the circle.
17. A *diameter* of the circle is any straight line drawn through the center and terminated in both directions by the circumference of the circle, and such a straight line also bisects the circle.
18. A *semicircle* is the figure contained by the diameter and the circumference cut off by it. And the center of the semicircle is the same as that of the circle.
19. *Rectilineal figures* are those which are contained by straight lines, *trilateral* figures being those contained by three, *quadrilateral* those contained by four, and *multilateral* those contained by more than four straight lines.
20. Of trilateral figures, an *equilateral triangle* is that which has its three sides equal, an *isosceles triangle* that which has two of its sides alone equal, and a *scalene triangle* that which has its three sides unequal.
21. Further, of trilateral figures, a *right-angled triangle* is that which has a right angle, an *obtuse-angled triangle* that which has an obtuse angle, and an *acute-angled triangle* that which has its three angles acute.
22. Of quadrilateral figures, a *square* is that which is both equilateral and right-angled; an *oblong that* which is right-angled but not equilateral; a *rhombus* that which is equilateral but not right-angled; and a *rhomboid* that which has its opposite sides and angles equal to one another but is neither equilateral nor right angled; and let quadrilaterals other than these be called *trapezia.*
23. Parallel straight lines are straight lines which, being in the same plane and being produced indefinitely in both directions, do not meet one another in either direction.

POSTULATES

Let the following be postulated:
1. To draw a straight line from any point to any point.
2. To produce a finite straight line continuously in straight line.
3. To describe a circle with any center and distance.
4. That all right angles are equal to one another.
5. That, if a straight line falling on two straight lines make the

116

interior angles on the same side less than two right angles, the two straight lines, if produced indefinitely, meet on that side on which are the angles less than the two right angles.

COMMON NOTIONS

1. Things which are equal to the same thing are also equal to one another.
2. If equals be added to equals, the wholes are equal.
3. If equals be subtracted from equals, the remainders are equal.
4. Things which coincide with one another are equal to one another.
5. The whole is greater than the part.

PROPOSITIONS

Prop. 1.   On a given finite straight line to construct an equilateral triangle.

Prop. 2.   To place at a given point (as an extremity) a straight line equal to a given straight line.

Prop. 3.   Given two unequal straight lines, to cut off from the greater a straight line equal to the less.

Prop. 4.   If two triangles have the two sides equal to two sides respectively, and have the angles contained by the equal straight lines equal, they will also have the base equal to the base, the triangle will be equal to the triangle, and the remaining angles will be equal to the remaining angles respectively, namely, those which the equal sides subtend.

Prop. 5.   In isosceles triangles the angles at the base are equal to one another, and, if the equal straight lines be produced further, the angles under the base will be equal to one another.

Prop. 6.   If in a triangle two angles be equal to one another, the sides which subtend the equal angles will also be equal to one another.

Prop. 7.   Given two straight lines constructed on a straight line (from its extremities) and meeting in a point, there cannot be constructed on the same straight line (from its extremities), and on the same side of it, two other straight lines meeting in another point and equal to the former two respectively, namely, each to that which has the same extremity with it.

Prop. 8. If two triangles have the two sides equal to two sides respectively, and have also the base equal to the base, they will also have the angles equal which are contained by the equal straight lines.

Prop. 9. To bisect a given rectilineal angle.

Prop. 10. To bisect a given finite straight line.

Prop. 11. To draw a straight line at right angles to a given straight line from a given point on it.

Prop. 12. To a given infinite straight line, from a given point which is not on it, to draw a perpendicular straight line.

Prop. 13. If a straight line set upon a straight line make angles, it will make either two right angles, or angles equal to two right angles.

Prop. 14. If with any straight line, and at a point on it, two straight lines not lying on the same side make the adjacent angles equal to two right angles, the two straight lines will be in a straight line with one another.

Prop. 15. If two straight lines cut one another, they make the vertical angles equal to one another.

Prop. 16. In any triangle, if one of the sides be produced, the exterior angle is greater than either of the interior and opposite angles.

Prop. 17. In any triangle two angles taken together in any manner are less than two right angles.

Prop. 18. In any triangle the greater side subtends the greater angle.

Prop. 19. In any triangle the greater angle is subtended by the greater side.

Prop. 20. In any triangle two sides taken together in any manner are greater than the remaining one.

Prop. 21. If on one of the sides of a triangle, from its extremities, there be constructed two straight lines meeting within the triangle, the straight lines so constructed will be less than the remaining two sides of the triangle, but will contain a greater angle.

Prop. 22. Out of three straight lines, which are equal to three given straight lines, to construct a triangle; thus, it is necessary that two of the straight lines taken together in any manner should be greater than the remaining one.

Prop. 23. On a given straight line and at a point on it to construct a rectilineal angle equal to a given rectilineal angle.

Prop. 24. If two triangles have the two sides equal to two sides respectively, but have the one of the angles contained by the equal straight lines greater than the other, they will also have the base greater than the base.

Prop. 25. If two triangles have the two sides equal to two sides respectively, but have the base greater than the base, they will also have the one of the angles contained by the equal straight lines greater than the other.

Prop. 26. If two triangles have the two angles equal to two angles respectively, and one side equal to one side, namely, either the side adjoining the equal angles, or that subtending one of the equal angles, they will also have the remaining sides equal to the remaining sides and the remaining angle to the remaining angle.

Prop. 27. If a straight line falling on two straight lines make the alternate angles equal to one another, the straight lines will be parallel to one another.

Prop. 28. If a straight line falling on two straight lines make the exterior angle equal to the interior and opposite angle on the same side, or the interior angles on the same side equal to two right angles, the straight lines will be parallel to one another.

Prop. 29. A straight line falling on parallel straight lines makes the alternate angles equal to one another, the exterior angle equal to the interior and opposite angle, and the interior angles on the same side equal to two right angles.

Prop. 30. Straight lines parallel to the same straight line are also parallel to one another.

Prop. 31. Through a given point to draw a straight line parallel to a given straight line.

Prop. 32. In any triangle, if one of the sides be produced, the exterior angle is equal to the two interior and opposite angles, and the three interior angles of the triangle are equal to two right angles.

Prop. 33. The straight lines joining equal and parallel straight lines (at the extremities which are) in the same directions (respectively) are themselves also equal and parallel.

Prop. 34. In parallelogrammic areas the opposite sides and angles are equal to one another, and the diameter bisects the area.

Prop. 35. Parallelograms which are on the same base and in the same parallels are equal to one another.

Prop. 36. Parallelograms which are on equal bases and in the same parallels are equal to one another.

Prop. 37. Triangles which are on the same base and in the same parallels are equal to one another.

Prop. 38. Triangles which are on equal bases and in the same parallels are equal to one another.

Prop. 39. Equal triangles which are on the same base and on the same side are also in the same parallels.

Prop. 40. Equal triangles which are on equal bases and on the same side are also in the same parallels.

Prop. 41. If a parallelogram have the same base with a triangle and be in the same parallels, the parallelogram is double of the triangle.

Prop. 42. To construct, in a given rectilineal angle, a parallelogram equal to a given triangle.

Prop. 43. In any parallelogram the complements of the parallelograms about the diameter are equal to one another.

Prop. 44. To a given straight line to apply, in a given rectilineal angle, a parallelogram equal to a given triangle.

Prop. 45. To construct, in a given rectilineal angle, a parallelogram equal to a given rectilineal figure.

Prop. 46. On a given straight line to describe a square.

Prop. 47. In right-angled triangles the square on the side subtending the right angle is equal to the squares on the sides containing the right angle.

Prop. 48. If in a triangle the square on one of the sides be equal to the squares on the remaining two sides of the triangle, the angle contained by the remaining two sides of the triangle is right.

Index